Life
Death

dipping our toes in the water ...

Second Edition

Regina Easley-Young
Bonnie Luft

Cover and title page image © 2015 Shutterstock, Inc.

Kendall Hunt
publishing company

www.kendallhunt.com
Send all inquiries to:
4050 Westmark Drive
Dubuque, IA 52004-1840

Copyright © 2010, 2015 by Regina Easley-Young and Bonnie Luft

ISBN 978-1-4652-7722-0

Kendall Hunt Publishing Company has the exclusive rights to reproduce this work,
to prepare derivative works from this work, to publicly distribute this work,
to publicly perform this work and to publicly display this work.

All rights reserved. No part of this publication may be reproduced,
stored in a retrieval system, or transmitted, in any form or by any
means, electronic, mechanical, photocopying, recording, or otherwise,
without the prior written permission of the copyright owner.

Printed in the United States of America

Contents

Contents

We want to give a special thank you to Joel Edwards for his artistic expertise and his unending patience. Joel enhanced the cover design, and created the original pen and ink drawings that occur throughout the book.

Acknowledgments

In Memory
Gwendolyn Pyron Easley
August 25, 1935-November 29, 1988

For their constant presence and encouragement, I am grateful for my husband, Doyle, and our son, Harrison. For our daughter and son-in-law, Meredith and Daniel, and our grandson, Noah Daniel, I give thanks.

Years of sitting at the bedside of the dying as a hospice chaplain proved to me that the dying and those who care for them are the experts. They were my teachers. I was there simply to bear witness to sacred and holy moments.

Regina Easley-Young, MDiv
Baylor University
Academic Support Programs
Academic Support Advisor for Student Outreach

In memory of my parents for the life they gave me and the guidance they provided throughout my life. With their death came a deeper understanding of what life is all about. The dedication is to the love of my life, my husband Gary, who was there throughout this venture providing love, support, and encouragement…I love you today and always! May this book provide you with support in knowing my desires and wishes at the end of my life. To our daughter and son, Amanda and Neil, who are so very special and important to me; to our son-in-law and daughter-in-law, Scott and Heather, who we love and are so honored to have as part of our family; and to our awesome grandchildren, who are such a joy in my life…it is my hope and prayer that someday this book will be a guide and source to their lives and to our generations beyond.

I love you…I love you more…I love you most!

Bonnie Luft
Mom and Nana

B.S., M.S.
Baylor University - Waco, Texas
Department of Health, Human Performance, and Recreation
Senior Lecturer
Adjunct Lecturer
40+ years of teaching

Introduction

This book is written in a practical and useful format with the hopes that it will provide beneficial and insightful information about the one universal experience that we all will share… death. This book is not intended to be merely a textbook that contains facts to memorize. Rather, it is aimed at assisting the learner with the adventure of exploring not only this engaging field of study, but also the adventure of exploring his or her own life. As such, it is to be a springboard for discussion and reflection, both for groups and for individuals. This book is intended to be used in a variety of educational settings such as universities, medical schools, hospitals, hospices, non-profit organizations, and possibly even some secondary schools. It goes without saying that the field of death education is far broader than we have written here. In making this acknowledgement, however, we have selected themes and provided resources that we trust will enhance knowledge, arouse curiosity, and supply useful tools throughout one's life. Each chapter is organized to include a *read, reflect, react, and recommended terms/important people/website* section. Following is an explanation of each chapter's format as it presents each topic:

READ

This section of the text presents fundamental and professional background information, conversations, helpful techniques, as well as stories on each selected topic. The information may stimulate the reader in developing or rethinking their opinions concerning life and death. The reading has the capacity to provoke thinking, inspire emotions, and encourage creative exploration that will guide, support, and enhance important decision-making that will occur in one's life.

Wider margins are provided for note taking.

REFLECT

This section presents insightful **questions** and thoughtful **quotes** that encourage one to reflect on their innermost feelings concerning life and death. The questions also stimulate an individual in reviewing the knowledge they gained in the **READ** section and may ultimately influence their choices and decisions.

REACT

This section provides hands-on activities that support the reading material. These activities allow an individual to react to life and death by completing written assignments, participating in partner or group discussions and activities, or actually performing in class scenarios. Written instructions include how to organize the group or class, plus the actions or rules for each activity.

RECOMMENDED TERMS/IMPORTANT PEOPLE/WEBSITES

This section presents a quick reference of terms from the **READ** section, names of well-known individuals in the field, and professionals who graciously provided expertise for the related topic; in addition, websites that can be used for gaining additional information.

NOTES

This section provides space for writing personal notes or recording information of special interest.

RESOURCES: FILMS

Chapter XV provides a list of possible films to view as a support and guidance in learning about the specific life and death topic.

Our hope is for the reader to gain academic and intellectual learning, as well as to foster a deep and enriched understanding of how life and death reflect one another. By gradually "dipping our toes in the water," there is the possibility of creating a more mature and reflective attitude on this sensitive subject. It is our sincerest wish for one to walk away with lessons that will be instrumental and fulfilling for life's final act.

I
Awareness of Death...
"Dipping our toes in the water"

Dying and Death Is About Living Life!

READ

Death is not an easy topic to talk about, but we make a start by "dipping our toes in the water." For example, the Greek origin of the word "Thanatology" is defined as "the study of death," but we do not stop there. Footstep by small footstep, we wade out toward the deep water, inching a step at a time, each toe testing the temperature, uncertain of what lies beneath our feet. We wonder if we will squish shifting sand, tread on slippery stones, or if the current will sweep us away. We feel the trickle of water between our toes. Before creeping on to the next step, we pause, feeling the fear of the unknown accompanying each movement. Then we take a deep breath to relax, understanding that with every unsteady footstep, the water feels warmer and more comfortable to our skin, giving us confidence that we are safe. It is the use of our senses that allows us to become aware of what is beneath the water as we walk into the unknown. Those same senses can help us increase our awareness into the forbidden topic of death. By enhancing our awareness of dying and death, hopefully, we can begin to feel more at ease with the unknown and accept it in our lives. Awareness is the beginning step that helps us to grow and increase our confidence, taking that same deep breath, and reassuring us that talking about death is acceptable.

We then ask ourselves the questions...How do we become aware of death? How do we learn that there is such a thing? Awareness is defined as "having the knowledge of something from observing it,

1

being told about it, or realizing that it is happening; being well-informed about the latest developments in the world of activity." We are surrounded by death and just do not realize it. Death is occurring everywhere, every minute. As children, we begin to be aware of death by losing a precious pet that we loved so dearly. We may hear a siren and feel a chill down our back immediately thinking that someone is hurt and may die. We may be driving and see a line of cars coming from a funeral led by a policeman on a motorcycle, making their way in a processional to the cemetery. Out of courtesy, we pull over to the side as a show of respect. We may drive by a serious accident and see that someone has died. If a natural or manmade disaster occurs, that devastating news is heard immediately around the world through the media. For example, Memorial Day is a day to honor our fallen soldiers who have given their lives serving our country. Even during special holidays, such as Thanksgiving, Christmas, or Easter, families gather, bringing back memories of a family member's life and death, and unknowingly, perhaps, increasing our awareness of death. Death is so close, yet so far away! When we have close encounters with death, we are forced to talk about it; but when death happens at a distance, we simply hear about it and then we seem to dismiss it from our minds. Recognition that death is all around us from an early age helps pave the foundation for how we begin to learn about dying and death.

Conversation may also be an influence on our awareness of death. It may begin by hearing our parents or friends talk about a death that has occurred. We listen to their words and we see their reactions. We observe the emotions that are taking place. We, ourselves, may be in conversation with others about a death that has happened. It may be a sudden death or one that had been expected. When people talk about death, we listen closely to their language and hear indirect or softer ways of expressing themselves regarding death. In other words, they "go in the back door" and avoid using the actual word "death" or "died." These disguises are euphemisms and one will often hear them used as a connecting link when talking about death, particularly as a spiritual or cultural expression. *A euphemism is "a synonym that is expressed in a vague, humorous, or even polite way for words or phrases considered to be difficult or harsh."* How we talk about death; how we listen to others' verbal expressions about death; how we observe our own and others' reactions to death all play a part in our awareness of how we move forward toward acknowledging the unfathomable reality of our own death.

Consider this scenario: You have been diagnosed with a terminal illness. The doctor relays the bad news using soft words, emphasizing the positive, explaining tests and treatments, and possible new interventions that may lead to remission. We look to our doctor for the reassurance and hope. But what happens on the receiving end? We may go into shock, not hearing the bad news, unable to comprehend what is being conveyed. Subconsciously, a wall goes up to block out the conversation. In an instant, we become helpless, filled with distress. We cannot even mutter the words, "I am dying." Then the questions arise...How do I tell my family? Do I hide the news? Do I just keep it within myself? What happens if I do not know the truth and only a member of my family knows about the terminal illness? Some people are in a situation where the facts are hidden or diluted or a barrier is formed. Some refuse to learn the facts. The patient wants to protect the family, and the family wants to protect the patient. The family may want to carry the whole burden. The family may want the patient to continue a new treatment. They may want to ask, "What is the next option?" We need to know that we all have the right to information on our health and the possible options involved. Shielding our loved ones from the truth only causes isolation and puts the patient in a bubble. In this type of situation, everyone involved—the doctor, the patient, and the family members—is blocking out important discussion on the end of life. What we do know is that the patient usually knows the truth better than anyone else does. Thus, the dying process has stepped into our lives and the awareness of death can no longer be denied.

From the time we are born, the dying process begins. Death will occur sometime in the future. As we carry on with our journey through life, whether due to a personal experience, or perhaps due to our own development, there will most likely be a point when we will begin to wonder, "What is dying?" and "What is death?" The definitions below may help in answering these two questions:

What is dying?

> *...to pass from physical life*
> *...to pass out of existence*
> *...to suffer a total and irreparable loss of action of vital functions*
> *...to cease to live*
> *...to perish*
> *...to pass from animate to a lifeless state*
> *...the process of passing from life or ceasing to be*
> *...the loss of life*
> *...the time when something ends*
> *...the act of expiring*

What is death?

> ...*the end of life*
> ...*the state of being dead*
> ...*the event of dying or departure from life*
> ...*the absence of life*
> ...*the time when something ends*
> ...*the act or state of passing from life*
> ...*a permanent cessation of all vital functions*
> ...*a final state*

As we begin to educate ourselves and learn about dying and death, we increase a firmer foundation toward appreciating and shaping our own death. In addition, we understand how the past, present, and future of our lives will help to show us the way toward greater self awareness. Below are some values that may be learned:

<u>Values we can gain from studying dying and death</u>

It helps us to…
1. better understand the grieving process.
2. deal with death in a more compassionate way.
3. better cope with our reactions to death.
4. better resolve guilt feelings.
5. focus our attention on relationships and their importance.
6. say the things that need to be said.
7. put a better perspective on emotional disturbing experiences.
8. make good final decisions.

These values will serve as a guide to how we think and to what we choose. Educating ourselves about our choices can lead us to make better decisions.

<u>Summary</u>

We will never have all the answers and we cannot redesign what we do not know. There is no quick way to understand death. We do know that sooner or later, dying will occur and death will happen. Awareness of death can be observed, felt, and heard throughout our lives. Whether it is in an event or in a conversation, *if we just begin to dip our toes in the water of death*, we can be the one who is in control using our increased awareness to be more prepared. It is that preparedness that will allow us to take that deep breath and hopefully, make the journey an easier and more comfortable experience in our lives. What if we live our lives as if we are going to die tomorrow? Being aware of dying and of death is about living and about life!

REFLECT

Questions to guide your reflection:

What are three examples that help one become aware of death?

*What is the first "picture" that comes to your mind when you hear the word **death**? Describe in detail.*

Who has influenced you the most in your beliefs about death? Why?

Have you had any death education? If so, where?

What values about death do you think you have at this point? How did you gain these values?

Where—what place—do you most associate with death in your life?

Quotes to ponder

In Death, Life is not over ... just changed."

REACT

Student Name: *Points:*

Class Time: *(Possible Pts.: _____)*

Activity   *Interviewing a "Senior Adult" About Life*

Instructions: 1. Read the "Interview" questions below.
2. Contact a person <u>age 70 years or older</u>........
    Introduce yourself.....Ask them if they would allow you to interview them about "life"....that the interview is for a "Death and Dying" class at Baylor University.
3. Make an appointment and ... if possible....go sit down with your chosen person..... (*You may want to review the questions again before your meeting)
4. Introduce yourself and tell them again what class this assignment is for.
5. Ask them <u>each</u> of the questions (# 1 to #10) below.
6. Write their response for each question... *this assignment does not need to be typed*

What was your first date? first car?

Secret to a happy marriage?

what world events impacted you most?

Childhood fear? Still there?

If you could change one thing about yourself...

In what ways is dad like you?

10-15 questions

7. *Due:* _____
   Day/Date of Interview? _____
   Name of Senior Adult? _____
   Age? _____
   Place of Interview? _____
   Relationship to you? _____
   Why did you select this person? _____

1. What was the most *fun thing* you did in your life?

2. What has been the *most useful/life changing invention* in our lifetime? Why?

3. What would you *advise me* to do in my *own lifetime*?

4. What is your *goal* in life? What do you think the *purpose in life* is?

5. What were *funerals* like when you were a kid?

6. What do you *believe* about an *afterlife*?

7. Do you *fear death*?

8. Do you *enjoy life*? Why or why not?

9. What have been some *dreams you have accomplished* so far in your life?

10. What is still on your "*bucket list*"?

Activity	***Euphemisms***

Instructions:	1. Divide the class into groups of four or five.
	2. Review the definition of "euphemism" above.
	3. Look at the examples of euphemisms.
	   • *Pushing up daisies*
	   • *Kicked the bucket*
	   • *Left this world*
	   • *Checked out*
	   • *Singing to the choir*
	4. See how many euphemisms your group can produce.
	5. Each group shares its euphemisms with the class to see how many different words or terms can be compiled.

Activity	***Sympathy Card***

Instructions:	Divide the class into small groups of four or five
	Each person will do the following:
	1. Choose or provide sympathy card. (website: Greetingsisland.com)
	2. State why you chose this particular card.
	3. Read the card aloud to the group.
	4. The listeners:
	   a. Listen to the card being read
	   b. List the feelings you are feeling.
	
	   I am feeling…
	   *
	   *
	   *
	   *
	
	5. Share thoughts and feelings.

Activity	***Read the book: <u>The Fall of Freddie the Leaf</u>*** Author Leo Buscaglia

Instructions:	Option 1: Reflective Adjectives
	1. At the end of a class, read aloud <u>The Fall of Freddie the Leaf</u>.
	2. As you read the book, have the students write the following:
	   a. Three or four events in the story.
	   b. List one or two adjectives to describe your emotions that you felt during each event listed in part a.
	3. Following the story, have students share their experiences.
	Option 2: Draw the story
	1. Provide class with blank paper and crayons or colored pencils.
	2. Have students draw their version of <u>The Fall of Freddie the Leaf</u>.

RECOMMENDED TERMS/ IMPORTANT PEOPLE/WEBSITES

<u>Terms</u>

Awareness: Having the knowledge of something from observing it, being told about it, or realizing that it is happening; being well-informed about the latest developments in the world of activity.

Euphemism: A synonym that is expressed in a vague, humorous, or even polite way for words or phrases considered to be difficult or harsh.

Thanatology: The study of death.

NOTES

II
Living Every Day...
"up close and personal"

READ

From the time we are born, we develop attitudes that affect our relationship to all areas of life. As our awareness of life and death develops through everyday experiences, so do our attitudes. The modeling by our parents and other family members; lessons from culture, religion, and traditions; conversations to which we are invited or from which we are excluded; language, both spoken and non-spoken...all of this is how our attitudes toward living and dying are developed. Our attitudes affect how well we live and how well we die.

In looking at how to live well, it is vital to remember that every day is a new day. We may ask the questions: "How can we live healthier?" "What is 'quality of life'?" "Do our attitudes help us to live well?" "If our attitudes do help us to live well, then how do they help us?" If we become unhealthy or have a terminal illness, each day can become more and more difficult, while at the same time becoming more and more precious. It is common to talk about one's quality of life and about living well with good health and a positive attitude, but we hear less about our quality of death and about dying well. Much of the time, we find ourselves ignoring conversations about death which may prohibit healthy attitudes from forming. We ask ourselves, then, "How do our attitudes about death and dying form?" "From where do these attitudes arise?" "How does death fit into life?"

How to live well . . . A story about the island of Ikaria

Adapted from: Dan Buettner's National Geographic article, "The Secrets of Living Longer." Dan Buettner, writer and adventurer, teamed with researchers to seek out the secrets of how to live longer by actually living among the people on the Greek island of Ikaria.

The Greek island of Ikaria is the newest of the "Blue Zones," which shows where people are living the longest. The native people of this island are adding more good years to their lives with a ratio of one in three living past the age of 90. What is it about this island that causes remarkable longevity? Why do Ikarians suffer 20 percent fewer cases of cancer, 50 percent lower rates of heart disease, one-ninth the rate of diabetes, and have almost no dementia or Alzheimer's disease compared to Americans? The island people escaped from pirates by moving their villages to the high rocky slopes. Because of this isolation, the people developed a constant confidence displaying positive attitudes and had a tendency to party. They go to bed late, sleep late, take daily naps, and may not open their stores until 11 a.m. Dan Buettner and the researchers dug deeper into their culture to try to find even more explanation for their long lives. What is the secret for this fountain of youth? Here is a list of factors with supporting statements that may contribute to this longevity:

- *Graze on wild greens:* May increase the level of antioxidants by 10%.
- *Strong sense of family and community living:* Provides power of love.
- *Throw out your watch:* Do not be owned by time; this lowers stress and reduces health issues like arthritis.
- *Nap daily:* A 30-minute nap decreases the risk of heart attack.
- *Walk where you are going:* Move naturally and walk whenever possible.
- *Phone a friend:* Social connections are proven to lower depression and mortality.
- *Drink goat's milk:* Contains the blood-lowering hormone tryptophan plus antibacterial compounds.
- *Maintain a Mediterranean diet:* Eat whole grains, fruits, vegetables, and fish avoiding red meat.
- *Enjoy Greek honey:* Local honey can provide antibacterial, anticancer, and anti-inflammatory conditions.
- *Open the olive oil:* Drizzle olive oil over foods after cooking.
- *Grow your own garden:* Fresh pickings are higher in compounds that decrease the risk of cancer and heart disease.
- *Get religion:* Go to religion services creating a faith-based life.
- *Bake bread:* Sourdough bread may improve glucose levels and steer off diabetes.
- *Drink Water:* Make sure your water has sufficient calcium and magnesium.
- *Eat 80%:* Know when you are 80% full – do not overeat.
- *Get a good night's sleep:* Recommends 6–8 hours of sleep to allow body to repair.

Living in a healthy way…

Our health is important to us. There is a saying, "We are what we eat," but it is more than that! It is a balance of nutrition and daily activity. Fitness is defined as *the endurance and stamina to withstand the physical and emotional stresses of daily life; being able to meet those emergency demands in life."* So, while forming positive attitudes about life will help us withstand the emotional stress of living, forming positive attitudes about death will help us withstand the emotional stress of dying. Whether it is our own death or someone else's, dying is definitely a stress on us physically, emotionally, and spiritually. Whether death is sudden or expected, we need to be ready to handle that stress when it appears in our lives. The healthier we are and the better shape we are in physically, emotionally, and spiritually, the better we can withstand the stresses that go along with death.

We know that lifestyle plays a big role in our makeup and in our quality of life. What we do and what we eat definitely affects our health. We all want to be happy and possess a high quality of well-being. It is worth a try to choose to live well.

<u>What is Quality of Life?</u>

Quality can be defined as *"good, competent, adequate, or having worth."* Life is defined as *"existence."* Life distinguishes a vital and functional being from a dead body, and involves the sequence of physical and mental experiences. Therefore, quality of life can be seen as the balancing of both the number of years in one's life and how those years are being lived. It is a measuring stick that assesses both the resources and the outcome that provide better health for an individual. It is our goal that healthy years will translate into helping us live a longer and more fulfilling life. What is your quality of life? How do you want to live your life? The quality of life you want is your choice.

Learning how to live well is a benefit we all need to know. We just need to put what we learn into action. The winning combination is diet and exercise and that develops healthy living which helps us stay well. Staying well helps us live well which helps us die well.

There are two Latin terms that provide us with an easy explanation of living and dying:

    Ars Vivendi: *The art of living*
    Ars Moriendi: *The art of dying*

If combined, these two statements may instruct us on how dying affects how we live: *"The art of dying teaches us the art of living."*

Where we acquire our attitudes about death

<u>Past Versus Present</u>

Our culture's attitudes toward death have changed quite dramatically over the past 100 years. To understand how these changes have affected us, we must look at life in the past compared to living in today's world.

First, our *life expectancy* has almost doubled due to knowledge that is now available at our fingertips, including advances in medicine, more research, better nutrition, and accessible education.

Second, the current *causes of death* have changed from infectious diseases that caused quick deaths, like smallpox or infant death, to chronic diseases that we may live with for years. Currently, cancer and heart disease are still the leading causes of death.

Third, the contrast of *geographical locations* has a definite influence on our attitudes. The turn of the twentieth century found our society a rural, agricultural one. Extended families lived within short distances from one another or lived together in the same house or on the same land. Family members did not move away for a career or to attend college, but they stayed close to home. In today's society, people may move to where they have a job, or, once graduated from high school, young adults move away to college, many times not returning home. Upon graduation from college, they may get married, find a job, and have to relocate to another place. Family ties may still be strong, but death is not as familiar and personal as it once was.

Fourth, *death is being taken from home*. Death has been removed from our living rooms into hospital rooms. It has been taken from "a natural part of life" to complicated ethical and moral decision making. More people are dying in institutions like hospitals and nursing homes more than they are dying at home. The discrepancy is that people say that they want to die at home, but they often do not get their choice.

This difference leads us to the last change, which deals with the *technology of today*. Hospitals and medical centers are equipped with the newest technologies that are available, so that is where we want to go to receive treatment for our illnesses. If this is where we come to the end of our lives and have not given thought to the choices we have about how to die, when to die, or even if to die; about whether we want to use life-extending technology, then instead of being dead when we're dead, we can be kept alive by state of the art technology.

We reflect on the past with its simplicity and stand in the present with its complications and know that both have powerful influence on our attitudes toward death. The chart below provides a quick way to look at the differences of yesterday and today.

	PAST	PRESENT
	1900	**2012**
1. Life Expectancy	47	78.8
2. Causes of Death	Infections and Diseases "Quick" May last days, weeks, or months	Heart disease and Cancer "Slow" May last years
3. Geographical Locations	Place and relatives Close family ties	Jobs and other roles Distance in family ties
4. Taking Death From Home	80 percent - Homes	80 percent - Institutions
5. Life-Prolonging Technology	"When you're dead, you're dead."	"When is dead?"

People

Who are the primary influences in our lives?
We begin with family as our primary influence, then we branch out to a broader spectrum that includes friends and other relationships. The development of religious beliefs, culture, education and our socioeconomic status all influence the foundation in the building of our attitudes toward life and toward death. When considering our families as our primary influences for every part of our lives, we must keep in mind that our families' attitudes were affected by their families, who were affected by their families, and so on. Not only is looking into our family's past an interesting task to undertake, but a responsible one, as well.

Why would I want to know my family history? What is genealogy? What is a family tree? Genealogy is *"the study of the history of families and the line of descent from their ancestors."* One of the main purposes of tracing one's family history is to determine any possible health issues that could be hereditary. Another purpose may be to know the cause and age of death and the place of burial. Do I want to be buried with the family? Searching our family background will allow us to know any marriages, interesting occupations, religions, or historical events. Yes, and sometimes we even uncover surprises. Some people will use a drawing of a tree to represent the many families that make up their ancestry. This family tree, which also can be a chart or table showing the line of descent from an ancestor, extends with its branches to show who is who in each family and the relationship to each other.

Learning about the past helps us appreciate how our current attitudes are influenced. We must know what happened yesterday to know why we think and react the way we do today. We have to ask the question… "What happened to make us think and feel the way we do?" We cannot change the past, but the present can be guided and formed by research, by new ideas, and even by those new people in our lives.

Fun thoughts on genealogy

> *"Tracing yourself back to better people."*
> *"I trace my family history so I will know who to blame."*
> *"Do I even WANT ancestors?"*
> *"Every family tree has some sap in it."*
> *"Friends come and go, but relatives tend to accumulate."*
> *"Everyone believes in it until their children act like fools."*
> *"I think my family tree is a few branches short of a full bloom."*
> *"If you go back far enough, we are all related."*

From family to friends to teachers, people definitely shape our lives. The people that surround us help to sculpt our values and beliefs, which affects our attitudes in life and death.

Music

For centuries, the topic of death has been a common element in music whether in writing the lyrics or in singing them. Singing seems to be one of those universal stress relievers and the artist provides that outlet for both public and private use. Music allows us to feel the mood by portraying the story or words in a rhythmic form. Historically, if death happens to a prominent person, then a song is written in that person's honor. A singer or songwriter may have a death occur to a special person in his or her life and a song is written about that experience. The words fill us with emotion, and those emotions affect our attitudes. Tears may even fill our eyes as we listen to the story being sung. The rhythm of music makes us sing and sway. We want to dance to the music. Some songs will tug at our hearts because they reach into our life experiences. How can this not affect our feelings, emotions, and attitudes about death?

Mass Media

From accidents to disasters and terrorism to wars, the media draws the picture for us to see the "death notice." Whether in the newspaper, technology, television, or radio, we are informed of the statistics and vital information almost as soon as it happens. Should the death stay private or should the public always be informed? Are we receiving the "real" picture? Is privacy being invaded? These questions make us realize it is evident that the media does affect our attitudes about death. It may be far away or in our own neighborhood, but they show us the picture and we try to get the feel for the "real" happening. We are continually teased by the media, and as a result, our attitudes are formed.

Literature

Whether it is prose or poetry, literature that delivers a story about dying affects our minds and may influence the development of our attitudes and how we look at death. Our minds expand creatively as we read and this allows us to enter the story and actually feel the pain and relive the portrayed life of the characters. We often feel a personal connection with the characters, or in poetry, with the words and phrases. Poetry lets our minds flow in rhythm or imagination with the words. That rhythm, like music, will affect how we feel about the message. Reading literature allows us to think privately and provides a silent way to learn about dying and death.

Language

We talked about euphemisms in the previous chapter to illustrate our discomfort in talking about death. When we find ourselves in an awkward situation, we may use these phrases to soften the feeling. At times, just using "plain talk" may be enough. Language can encourage us to talk about death. It might be to get or give information. If a person is surrounded daily with death as in war or a medical occupation, he or she will consider the language about death a natural part of conversation. People in these occupations must tell it like it is. It does not mean the person becomes hardened to death, it just means that he or she can talk more freely about the subject because it is part of the daily routine. On the other hand, when a person is not around death, he or she is allowed to avoid it or mask it in some way. Language, whether easy or difficult, does influence our attitudes.
(examples: "KIA" or "body count")

Humor

Humor does have a place in talking about death. It often provides that outlet for us to talk about this unmentionable topic. Humor may serve as a pain reliever, but laughter is a stress reliever. Humor may provide that sense of control that is often desired. Hearing and participating in laughter always serves as a great leveler. At a social event, there is nothing like a good laugh to bring people together. In a dying situation, memories are often reflected and there may be that one funny incident that causes a few chuckles. Laughter can cause the body to relax, which in turn provides calmness that may be needed during the stressful time of death. Humor may offer that outlet to people who care for the dying day in and day out—it may just be what is needed to get through the day. Humor gives us that distance from the difficulty of death and allows a rebounding affect after the event. There is nothing like a good laugh to make one feel better even in a sad situation.

Entertainment

(Movies – Television –Video Games)
These modes of entertainment may feature death or dying in some way. If we see an advertisement of a movie or a television program

that has death involved, that seems to "lure us in" to watch the show. Death scenes captivate the audience. Even cartoons portray death, but they present death as being reversible. With children, we have to be careful of this reversible death. A child may think that if someone dies, he or she can return to life. Seeing an abundance of unrealistic scenes of aggression may cause a person to be less sensitive when he or she actually sees or is involved in the "real" event. Is our technology-saturated society so enchanted with death that we must hear or see it daily? Whether or not entertainment affects our attitudes about death is something of which to be aware in ourselves.

Art

The talent of an artist can take our breath away. As we stare into the art, we can dream and imagine with our mind's eye. From painting and drawing to sculpture, the beauty of fine art may depict any theme or story. Whether it is death or another event, the actual viewing of art in various forms allows us to express feelings that possibly need to be exposed. Rembrandt was known to express suicide and sadness in his artistry. Symbolic art forms—like memorial quilts, scrapbooks, and commemorative walls—bring national unity and allows family ties to be kept using art as a form of mourning. The use of hands and eyes can bring those memories to light. Art does, indeed, affect our attitudes about death.

Summary… putting the body and mind together

The mind is a wonderful thing. Our minds affect our attitudes, and our attitudes affect our minds. When we are healthy, our minds are clear; when we are ill, our minds can grow blurry. It is hard to think when we hurt. We have heard the saying, "mind over body." This is true…the mind is affected by the body and the body is affected by the mind. There is a formula that one can use to illustrate this: _Illness and chronic pain = depression and anxiety = disease._ There are stories told where positive thinking during an illness had a direct influence on the body and how quickly the healing took place.

Negative thoughts, on the other hand, do take a toll on the body by causing stress, and stress can cause negative reactions in the body. It can cause the healing process to be slow or not to happen at all. Similarly, negative attitudes can put a distance between death and us because we fear that if we get as close as talking about our own death, then we just might die. Those attitudes may cause discomfort. That discomfort doesn't even begin to describe how uncomfortable some people are when they talk about death.

In talking about positive attitudes, we know that expressions of love, friendship, and positive energy can help one battle the disease or illness and can lead one down the path to health. There is nothing better than a hug, a touch, or a compliment to make one feel better! This can lead to a desire for hope. Hope is essential to everyone, especially to the dying patient. How does one form a positive attitude in death?

Hope is the beginning. Spirituality and religious beliefs can provide an important outline and context for our death and can be an ingredient in the development of our attitudes. Radiating a positive attitude can be an asset for caregivers as they listen to us, know where our hope lies, support our goals, and reassure us that they will be with us for this final journey.

As we look at how to live well and how our attitudes are formed, we see that they go hand in hand. From the influences of our past to those special people in our lives and with the impact of music, art, and literature, our attitudes are continually forming. We do not have the opportunity for our life to be a dress rehearsal; we cannot practice, die, and then come back for the real show. This is it! If we know how to live well, we know how to die well. We must *live everyday up close and personal* and meet the challenge of death.

REFLECT

Questions to guide your reflection:

Who are the primary influences in your life regarding the development of your attitudes toward death?

Which events in your life have affected your attitude in death the most?

In what ways do you keep death at an arm's distance in your life?

At what age do you really expect to die?

What are three ways you can have a healthier life?

What are three activities that you can do to be more fit?

What is quality of life for you?

What are your attitudes toward death? Name three.

Quotes to ponder

"Nobody said life would be easy, they just promised it would most likely be worth it."

"Life is like a box of chocolates….You never know what you are going to get." Forest Gump.

"You live what you learn."

"You cannot relive yesterday."

"Secret to life: 1 Think….That is what you need to figure out."

REACT

Activity   *Category Comparison*

Instructions: Compare the categories in the chart "Past and Present."
Reflect on each category:

1. Why did death occur at this early age in 1900?
2. Why has the average age of death increased?
3. What were the primary infectious diseases that were the causes of death in the year 1900?
4. In addition to the primary causes of death mentioned for the year 2012, list the top 10 causes of death in the year 2012.
5. For the category, "Geographical Mobility," compare how these different attitudes toward mobility have affected how familiar our culture is with death.
6. Reflect on the following statements:
   One hundred years ago, death occurred at home.
   Today, death occurs in institutions even though 90 percent of people want to die at home.
7. How do you see the increase in technology affecting our attitudes and treatment of death?

Activity   *Lifeline**

Instructions: 1. Draw your lifeline.
2. Draw a line, either horizontally or vertically.
   - At one end, place a mark indicating your birthdate and birthplace.
   - At the other end, place a mark indicating your date and place of death.
   - In between, indicate places on your lifeline where significant events have happened in your life, events that have changed you, made a difference to you. These should be placed on the first part of your life.
   - On the second part of your lifeline, indicate your goals and dreams. What do you want your future to look like? What do you want to accomplish? Include the deaths of your parents and grandparents on this part of your lifeline. How do you want the end of your life to look?

   <u>What to include – the significant events in your life</u>

You:	Birth–Childhood–High School–College
	Career–Marriage–Deaths (grandparents/parents)
	Future Dreams?
Children:	Birth – Childhood – High School – School/College
	Career – Marriage – Deaths

*From *Thanatopics: Activities and Exercises for Confronting Death* by J. Eugene Knott, Mary C. Ribar, Betty M. Duson, Marc R. King. Copyright © 1991 by J. Eugene Knott, Mary C. Ribar, Betty M. Duson, Marc R. King. Reprinted by permission of the author.

Grandchildren: Childhood – High School – School/College
                              Career–Marriage
Retirement: What will you do? Hobbies? Travel? etc.
Death: When? – How? – What age?

Activity   ***Longevity – Estimating Your Life Expectancy***

Instructions: Look at the questions below–record your answers in the blank on the right. If a particular item does not apply to a participant or call for a math change, go to the next statement. Keep a running tally!

* In top blank, start with the following age: Females: 81/Males: 76

Questions to ask yourself:	Start with:	
		76
1. If you are a female – add 4 / male – subtract 3		73
2. If you are over 35 now - add 1; if over 65 - add 3		73
3. If you are non-white, subtract 1		72
4. If any grandparent lived to 85 – add 2. If all 4 lived to at least 80 – add 4		76
5. If any parent died of stroke/heart attack before age 60 – subtract 3		76
6. If any parent/sibling has/had cancer/heart ailment – subtract 2		76
7. If any parent/sibling has/had diabetes – subtract 2		76
8. If you are over 60, are active/working at something you enjoy – add 2		78
9. If you completed college – add 1		78
10. If you completed a graduate degree – add 2		78
11. If you live in an urban(city) area – subtract 2		78
12. If you live in a town of fewer than 30,000 people – add 1		79
13. If you work at a sedentary job – subtract 2		79
14. If you get moderate to vigorous exercise for 20-30 minutes at least 3 times per week – add 3		82
15. If you are married – add 2		82
16. Female, age 23-53 – subtract 1 for each 5 years you have lived alone Male, age 23-53 – subtract 2 for each 5 years you have lived alone		82
17. Sleep: If you sleep 6-8 hours most nights – add 2 If you routinely get fewer than 6 or more than 8 hours of Sleep – subtract 3		84
18. If you are basically satisfied with life – add 2; if not – subtract 2		86
19. Are you basically angered and explosive in your responses? If yes – subtract 3 / if not – add 2		88

20. Driving: If you have had a speeding ticket in the
    past year – subtract 1   _88_

21. Seatbelts: If you always wear your seatbelt–add
    1 / if not–subtract 1   _89_

22. Drinking: If you drink more than 2 alcoholic beverages
    a day or more than fourteen in a week – subtract 3   _89_

23. Smoking: If you smoke more than 10 cigarettes
                a day – subtract 3   _92_
                If you smoke more than 20 a day – subtract 5
                If you quit smoking over 2 years ago – add 2
                If you have never smoked – add 3

24. Weight: Overweight by 50 pounds – subtract 4   _92_
                Overweight by 30 – 49 pounds – subtract 3
                Overweight by 15-29 pounds – subtract 2

25. Diet: If you have a low fat, high fiber diet – add 3   _89_
                If a high fat, low fiber, or both – subtract 3

26. Medical Checkups: _90_
    Female: If you have a pap smear at least every
                2 years – add 2
                If you perform a monthly breast
                self-exam – add 2
    Male: If you do a regular testicular
                self-exam – add 1
                If after age 40, you have your prostate
                checked – add 1

27. Drugs: If you use mood-lifting medications   _90_
                regularly–subtract 2

28. Blood Pressure: If you know your blood pressure –
                       add 1   _91_
                       If it is within normal limits – add
                       1 more

29. Cholesterol: If you know your cholesterol – add 1   _91_
                       If it is under 200 – add 1 more

30. Friendships: If you are a loner – lacking 2
                       friends – subtract 2   _91_

31. Engaging in risky activities: _91_
                If you own a gun – subtract 1
                If you engage in sky diving – subtract 1
                If you engage in scuba diving – subtract 1
                If you hitchhike – subtract 1
                If you ride a motorcycle – subtract 1
                If you race motor vehicles – subtract 1
                Have you bungee jumped? – subtract 1

TOTAL: "Calculated" life expectancy figure   _91_

Circle any statements where you lost points.

Circle any statements that could be possible life-style changes.

Activity   *Your Genealogy*

Instructions: What: Research back 4 generations of your family. Start with **"You"**
                     Purpose: 1. To trace back to any health issues that might be hereditary
                              2. To learn the causes of deaths
                              3. To discover burial places of family
                              4. To look back at any significant family history
                              5. To determine any family traits
                              6. To provide family history to future generations
                     How: Contact any family member and/or do research on the internet.
                     Format: Must be typed!
                     Suggestion: Table, Word Document, Columns, or be creative

Genealogy Project Due:_____

What to include: 1. Date of project
                     2. Four generations: Both sides of family (See list
                         "*People to Include*" below)
                     3. 4 sections to the assignment (**If typing full title/
                         topic, there will be 3 sections*)

Section 1:   **Legend or key for codes**
              If you decide to use "codes," a legend must be included. (*See
              below*)
              If you type the "*full title or topic*," then you would *not* need a
              legend/key of explanation.

Section 2:   **Tree or Bracket** (*Internet is a good source to find examples*)
              Include: Both sides of family
              Names on tree or bracket
              Label Relationship: May use codes below or type out.
                                   (*See below*) If information is "Not
                                   Available": Type "NA" (*Explanation
                                   will be later*)

Section 3:   **Charts or some organized typed information– "4 Generations"**
              (**See list of "People to include" below*)
              List "Maternal Side" Together (*7 people*)
              List "Paternal Side" Together (*7 people*):
              You: Include "You" in the chart or document
              (*Total: Maternal 7 + Paternal 7 + You = 15 people*)
              Label Relationship: May use codes below or type out.
              (*See below*)
              For each person: List 12 "Facts" (*See list of required "Facts"
              below*)
              *Unavailable Information: If information is not available,
                                   type "NA."
              *Must include a note of explanation.
              State the reason why information could not be found or why
              it is not available.
              Where to type note: Type at bottom of that family's chart.
              *"Date of Death": If person is living, type "Still alive."

Section 4: **Character Traits and Heath Issues**
1. List any "health issues" that you could possibly inherit
2. List any "character traits" that you possess.
   List the trait and which side of the family.
   (*Example: nose – Father's side / widow's peak – Mother's side*)

People and Codes to include in the Genealogy Project:

Maternal Side: Mother's	Code:	Paternal Side: Father's	Code:
Maternal Grandmother:	mGma	Paternal Grandmother:	pGma
Maternal Grandfather:	mGpa	Paternal Grandfather:	pGpa
Maternal Great Grandmother:	mGGma	Paternal Great Grandmother:	pGGma
Maternal Great Grandfather:	mGGpa	Paternal Great Grandfather:	pGGpa

Codes:

Maternal Side:		*Paternal Side:*	
mGma:	Maternal Grandmother	pGma:	Paternal Grandmother
mGpa:	Maternal Grandfather	pGpa:	Paternal Grandfather
mGGma:	Maternal Great Grandmother	pGGma:	Paternal Great Grandmother
mGGpa:	Maternal Great Grandfather	pGGpa:	Paternal Great Grandfather

---

Total: Maternal 7 + Paternal 7 + You = 15 people

YOU

Mother	*Father*
*mGma * mGpa*	*pGma * pGpa*
*mGGma/mGGpa * mGGma/mGGpa*	*pGgma/mGGpa * pGgma/pGGpa*

Facts to include: ✦relations		**Possible code to use:**
✓ 1.	Full Name: First – Middle – Maiden – Married	
	(*If no middle name, include a note to explain*)	
2.	Date of birth	DOB
3.	Place of birth	POB
4.	Date of Marriage	DOM
5.	Place of Marriage	POM
6.	Occupation/Vocation	VOC
7.	Date of Death	DOD
8.	Age of Death	AOD
9.	Cause of Death	COD
10.	Place Buried	PB
11.	Number of years between wife/husband's death	YBD
	Note: Subtract "Year of death" for each person in the couple	
12.	Number of children/miscarriages	C/M

OPTIONAL FACTS:

13.	Religion	RE
14.	Fun Fact	FF

Activity	***Add a Little Laughter***

Instructions:	1. Have the class bring a joke or a YouTube site about death to the next class.
	2. The next day, let volunteers share their joke or site.
	3. When volunteers have presented their laughter for the day, have the class do the following:
	   a. Laugh for 1 minute.
	   b. Ask the following questions:
	     How do you feel?
	     How does your body feel?
	     How is this different from being sad?

Activity	***What is the name?***
Instructions:	Divide the group into groups of four to five participants Using small group discussion with each other: Name three <u>examples for each</u> of the following categories: 1. Songs that were written about death 2. Recent disasters 3. Cartoons that include death 4. Novels that include death Reflection: 1. How quickly did you come up with the answers for each category? 2. Which category brought back the saddest memories? 3. Which novel had the happiest ending? 4. Which of your three disasters was the worse? Why?

RECOMMENDED TERMS/ IMPORTANT PEOPLE/WEBSITES

Terms

Ars Vivendi:	The art of living.
Ars Moriendi:	The art of dying.
Family tree:	A chart or table that shows the line of descent from ancestors, especially that of a specific person or family.
Fitness:	The endurance and stamina to withstand the physical and emotional stresses of daily life; being able to meet emergency demands in our life.
Genealogy:	The study of the history of families and the line of descent from their ancestors.
Life expectancy:	The estimated number of years remaining in a person's life at a particular time.
Longevity:	The average number of years between birth and death.
Morbidity:	Illness.
Mortality:	Death.
Mortality Rate:	Also known as death rate—the measure of the number of people who have died within a particular time period compared to the number of people in the population.
Life:	Existence in the physical world; the time someone is alive.
Quality:	Degree of value or worth.
Quality of life:	The balance of life and quality together; a yardstick that measures either the continued day to day living, or the outcome at the end of life, of how someone has lived his or her life.

Websites

Dan Buettner. "The Secrets of Living Longer." National Geographic, 2005 and 2012.

NOTES

III
Fears of Death...
"Do we have to talk about THAT?"

READ

We hesitate to discuss our fears; at the end of life however, it is almost certain that fear will emerge. Many people say that their greatest fears of death are being alone and being in pain. When they are nudged to dig deeper about why they fear death, their responses go something like this:

> *"I am afraid of dying alone."*
> *"I am afraid of dying in pain."*
> *"I am not afraid of death; I am afraid of dying."*
> *"I fear what happens after death....what is beyond this life?"*

Elderly people often find themselves living alone. They may live by themselves or with family. Family and friends may live far away or they may have already died. Assisted living facilities or in-home assistance can solve this loneliness somewhat, but most elderly do not want to move from their homes or have another person living with them. Love and support from others will help the path seem easier. However, we must be aware that there is no guarantee that we will have someone with us at the time of death.

Pain is a synonym for suffering. When people state their fear of pain, it is often accompanied by, "I don't want to suffer."

29

With the right medical choices, pain can be alleviated. Some of these choices will be discussed in a later chapter.

The unknown process of dying is another common fear. Every death is different because we are each unique. Some deaths are slow, and some deaths are quick. It may not be easy for medical professionals to predict what course the dying process will take or when it will occur. At other times, one's dying process may be fairly predictable, depending on the disease and the individuality of the person. We have professionals who can give us their opinions and provide us guidance and choices, but we must remember that it is often an educated guess. We may be told that we have two days to live, and we live thirty days, or they may tell us we have six months to live, and we die in one month. We understand that we will die, but we must acknowledge that the process of how we get to death will be unclear. We cannot control when or how death will happen, but what we can do is be better prepared until that moment.

To acknowledge our death is to raise our beliefs and questions about life after death. We have heard stories where people say they have seen the light at the end of the tunnel, and they return to tell their story. What is on the other end of the tunnel? We just do not know. From reincarnation to outer body experiences, the afterlife is a mystery. The unknown may fill us with fear. We all wish our deceased relatives or friends could tell us what it is like, but we will all have to wait to find the answer to the unknown.

Learning to live with our fears and managing our fears in a healthy manner can only be positive, especially as we learn that others share in our fears. We may live for years never acknowledging these fears, but by not sharing our fears of death, we may grow isolated and vulnerable; by being transparent in sharing our fears, we may cause someone else to feel uncomfortable. We might even think that by talking about our fears of death it just might come true—a jinx, in other words.

If we have a fear of roller coasters due to heights or speed, it is easy to flee and just not ride the ride, but we cannot flee death. The only way to begin to handle our anticipated death in a skillful manner is to face our fears and begin to accept the reality that death will definitely come to each of us.

<u>Let's look at why we dread death</u>

We do not know when or how.
We do not want to be a burden to our family.
We do not know what will happen to our family.
We are not finished yet—we still have work to be done and life to live.
We do not want to feel sad.
We do not want a life-threatening disease.
We do not know what others will say about us.
We imagine the process of dying to be painful and difficult.
We do not want to be alone.
We do not want people to treat us differently.
We do not want to see the death of someone we love.
We do not know what lies ahead.

<u>What can we do to face our fears of death?</u>
We must acknowledge that by not addressing these fears and the reality of death that we just might miss out on one of the most meaningful experiences of life. In order to face our fears, we must begin by using simple conversations, whether it be with family or friends. It is a sensitive topic that needs to come to the forefront in order for us to know our available choices, make decisions, and be more prepared for that special event.

We do not want to miss it!
If you are asked the question, "Do we need to talk about death?"
The answer is "Yes."
It is a part of life!

REFLECT

Questions to guide your reflection:

*Name five of your fears related to death.

*Reflect on the previous chapter addressing:
> *1. How do people and events affect our attitudes?*
> *2. Do you see any correlation between your fears of death and the attitudes that you have developed?*

*Reflect on these five questions on the afterlife:
> *1. What happens to us when we die?*
> *2. If we turn into dust compost, what is the point?*
> *3. Why are we here?*
> *4. What difference does it make?*
> *5. What do you want to accomplish while you are on this brief stage?*

Quotes to ponder:

"It's not what you look at that matters …. it is what you see!"

"Death is only the beginning."

"The fear of aging is when life does not have meaning."

REACT

Activity   *Creating an Acronym*

Instructions: 1. Divide the class into groups of four to five students.
                   2. Have each group look at the following acronym:
                       F -   Flee
                       E -   Erase
                       A -   Anticipate
                       R -   Response
                   3. As a group, create an acronym for FEAR.
                       You may <u>not</u> use any of the words in the above acronym.

Activity   *Opening Windows**

Instructions: 1. Divide the class into partners.
                   2. Tell your partner about your first death experience.
                   3. Have each set of partners join another set of partners.
                   4. Each person in the group of four:
                       a. Tell the story about your very first experience with death.
                       Instructor: Ask if anyone wants share his or her story.
                       b. State what <u>is frightening</u> to you about dying.
                       Instructor: Ask groups for answers.
                                      Write answers on board.
                                      How many are the same?
                       c. State what <u>is not frightening</u> to you about dying.
                       Instructor: Ask groups for answers.
                                      Write answers on board.
                                      How many are the same?
                       d. What is your <u>belief</u> about the afterlife?
                       Instructor: Ask groups for answers.
                                      How many different ideas?

Activity   *Imagining Your Own Death*

Instructions: 1. Have class put their heads down on desk.
                   2. Turn out the lights.
                   3. Instructions to students:
                       a. Close your eyes.
                       b. Let your day's schedule roll around. Pause.
                       c. Try to let those concerns leave your mind. Pause.
                       d. Try to relax and let your imagination take over.
                       e. You predicted your death earlier.
                       f. Imagine that day has arrived, whether it be a terminal
                          illness, a car accident, a fall, or just old age.

*From *Thanatopics: Activities and Exercises for Confronting Death* by J. Eugene Knott, Mary C. Ribar, Betty M. Duson, Marc R. King. Copyright © 1991 by J. Eugene Knott, Mary C. Ribar, Betty M. Duson, Marc R. King. Reprinted by permission of the author.

g. Where are you?
   What happened?
   What is wrong?
   How do you feel?
   How do you look?
   Who is there with you?
   Are you in pain?
   Are you being taken care of?
   Are your affairs in order?
   How long have you been there?
   What is happening to your body?
   Are you comfortable?
   Do you have any fears?
   Is there someone who is not there that you want there?
   Are there any machines?
   What are you worrying about?
   Are you close yet?
   What is happening to your body?
   Are you where you want to be?
   How is your comfort level?
   You are getting close.......
   What are you thinking?
   Your breathing is slowing down—very shallow.
   You have no movement left in your body.
   Your heart is slowing down.
   One last breath.
   You're gone.
4. Let students keep heads down for 5 minutes.
5. Debriefing Questions: Debriefing may be performed in a class, in groups of 3 or 4, or by writing reflective answers.
   a. What was the experience like for you?
   b. Was any part of your fantasy meaningful?
   c. Did you discover any preferences regarding your death?
   d. Did anything about the way you are living your life become clearer to you?
   e. Did you discover any unfinished business that you might like to pursue?
   f. What about the people in your life?
   g. Was your death what you expected?
   h. Would you like to share any part of your fantasy?
   i. What about your fears? Any new fears?
   j. What about afterlife?

Activity   *The Station*

Instructions: Note: This activity is best done at the end of a class or session.
1. Have class put their heads down with eyes closed.
2. Turn lights out. Let your imagination go.
3. Read the following story: *The Station,* then dismiss class.

The Station by Robert J. Hastings*

Tucked away in our subconscious is an idyllic vision. We see ourselves on a long trip that spans the continent. We are traveling by train. Out the windows we drink in the passing scene of cars on nearby highways, of children waving at a crossing, of cattle grazing on a distant hillside, of smoke pouring from a power plant, of row upon row of corn and wheat, of flatlands and valleys, of mountains and rolling hillsides, of city skylines and village halls.

But uppermost in our minds is the final destination. On a certain day, at a certain hour, we will pull into that station. Bands will be playing and flags waving. Once we get there so many wonderful dreams will come true, and the pieces of our lives will fit together like a completed jigsaw puzzle.

How restlessly we pace the aisles, wasting the minutes away with loitering – waiting, waiting, waiting for the station.

"When we reach the station, that will be it!" We cry.
"When I'm 18."
"When I buy a new Mercedes Benz!"
"When I put the last kid through college."
"When I have paid off the mortgage!"
"When I reach the age of retirement, I shall live happily every after!"

Sooner or later we must realize there is no station, no one place to arrive at once and for all. The true joy of life is the trip. The station is only a dream. It constantly outdistances us.

"Relish the moment" is a good motto, especially when coupled with Psalm 118:24: "This is the day which the Lord hath made; we will rejoice and be glad in it." It isn't the burdens of today that drive men mad. ***It is the regrets over yesterday or the fear of tomorrow. Regret and fear are twin thieves who rob us of today.***

So, stop pacing the aisles and counting the miles. Instead, climb more mountains, eat more ice cream, go barefoot more often, swim more rivers, watch more sunsets, laugh more, cry less.

Life must be lived as we go along. The station will come soon enough.

*From *A Penny's Worth of Minced Ham, Another Look at the Great Depression;* Copyright © 1986 by Southern Illinois University Press.

RECOMMENDED TERMS/ IMPORTANT PEOPLE/WEBSITES

Terms

Fear: An emotion experienced in anticipation of some specific pain or
                              danger, usually accompanied by a desire to flee or fight.

NOTES

IV
Good Death...
"Is there such a thing?"

READ

Is there such a thing as a good death? What do we mean by this?
Is there such a thing as a bad death?
Do we ever think about how we want to die?
Can we really control how we die?

These are some questions that we normally do not think about, much less talk about.

A good death includes the physical, emotional, social, and spiritual parts of one's life. In order to discuss what a good death is, we begin by discussing the physical. In looking at the physical side of death, it is important to note that death does not look like what is portrayed in movies or on television. Even though it is hoped for, one's death is not necessarily calm and peaceful. It can be sudden, violent, or even slow when it involves a long-term illness.

A dying person may look thin, pale, and tired, or he or she may drift in and out of consciousness. With weakness and possible disfigurement from surgery, one may have nausea with possible strained and irregular breathing. One's final moments of breathing may include a noisy sound called a <u>death rattle</u>, or breathing may just stop. The body's muscles will become relaxed with involuntary contractions. These observations make up only a snapshot of how death is sometimes experienced. There may not be an easy way out of this world that one has entered.

⚹We are created to live. Every part of our body fights to live. While our bodies struggle to live, we exhibit emotions that are woven into our lives and give depth to our moments. If the dying person has had time to struggle with and come to peaceful terms with his or her death, he or she may gaze into the distance. There may be an experience of private emotions. It is not surprising for the dying person to show tears of regret and gratitude, fear and joy, anxiety and peace.

⚹Anger, depression, and fear are not uncommon, and should not to be dismissed. These emotions can appear as part of the reflection upon one's life and death. From hugs and caresses to tending to physical needs, the final moments of living can be significant and memorable events that are sweet, tender, and beautiful.

⚹For the dying person, coming to terms with the spiritual issue of identity can be helpful in easing the passage to death. Most of our lives are lived with our identities being defined by what we do, by what we accomplish, or by the titles we are given. If a grandfather has worked for more than 30 years as a well-loved high school football coach, and due to his terminal illness he finds himself in bed unable to do anything except lie still, he might begin to ask these questions⚹"Who am I now? I can't move my body much less throw a football anymore. I can't play with my grandchildren. I can't bring home a paycheck. What is my life worth?"

⚹When we are stripped of the things that make up who we are in our daily lives—the things that make us wife, mother, husband, father, student, professional, friend, sister, son, daughter, or any number of roles we live by—we may begin to question our identity⚹So much of the meaning of our lives is made up of our relationship with others, and while we may intuitively know that it is not *what* someone does with us or for us that makes them precious to us, it is precisely those things that make up the memories we share. Of course, we remember playing catch with our son, holding and soothing our hurt children, the shopping trip with friends, and the accolades from the family about the annual holiday dinner. These things are the "stuff" of life. However, it is not all of who we are. It is only part of who we are, for it is the doing—it is all of those roles we play, the relationships into which we pour our lives —that comes out of who we are. And so when facing the end of our lives and the end of our "doing," we may begin to wonder just what it is that makes our life meaningful. Our lives have transitioned from being independent to being dependent…from taking care of others to being taken care of⚹from doing to simply being. Because "simply being" is not valued as much as the "busy doing" of our lives, we often find ourselves at a loss for how to live. And so we begin to question our identity. However, it is when we detach from the activities, roles, and busyness of our lives that we can then begin to catch sight of just who we are. There is nothing to cover up our inner lives anymore. The silence of the soul becomes very real. It can cause some anxiety if one is not prepared; but with time, encouragement, and the continued presence of loved ones, death can grow into peace and contentment.

However, awareness of the physical, emotional and spiritual characteristics of death does not mean that we have complete control of all areas of our death.

The "Diamond Concept"
This concept is a way to visualize how the physical, emotional, spiritual, and social aspects are connected in the journey to a good death.

There are some things that we just cannot know:

- *How quickly or slowly death happens?*
- *Where will death happen: at home or in the hospital?*
- *Being alone or not being alone?*
- *Knowing what is comfortable?*
- *Talking or not talking about it?*
- *Whether a celebration or whether intolerable or both?*
- *Whether taxing or debilitating?*
- *Whether accepted or denied?*

Reflecting on these questions can help us more fully realize how we want to experience our own death.

When does "dying well" begin?

- *Long before death happens...*
- *Prior to brain damage or before a coma sets in...*
- *Prior to medical treatment decisions being made...*
- *Prior to administering treatment...*

So, what are the important things in "dying well?"

- *Being prepared...*
- *Having loved ones support...*
- *Having the best death for us...*
- *Knowing that there is no right or wrong path to choose...*

From the perspective of the dying person, in her book, *Talking About Death Won't Kill You,* Virginia Morris offers a list of "Principles of a Good Death."

1. **Realize that death is coming**… to understand what is expected.
2. Be afforded **dignity and privacy.**
3. Have a **choice where death occurs.**
4. Have **access to information and expertise** about what is needed. (*Helpline: "211"*)
5. Have **adequate control over physical pain relief and symptom management.**
6. Receive equal attention for **emotional and spiritual pain.**
7. Have **access to hospice/palliative care** in any location.
8. Have a choice about **who is present and who shares the moment of death.**
9. **Issue advance directives** that will provide reasonable control of what happens and will ensure the respect of one's wishes and choices.
10. Have **time to say good-bye.**
11. Be able **to let go** and not have life prolonged pointlessly.

Talking About Death Won't Kill You also provides some insight into appropriate answers to the following questions:

What can a caregiver or friend offer the dying patient on the way to a good death?

1. *Offer friendship for loneliness.*
2. *Offer friendship for fear.*
3. *Remind the patient that he or she will not be forgotten.*
4. *Convince the patient that his or her loved ones will be fine.*
5. *Know that medications also include human touch and compassion.*
6. *Know that pain control is an integral part of patient care.*
7. *Support by being present, if patient desires.*

What can you do while visiting a dying person in his or her last moments?

1. *Sit beside the person.*
2. *Take the dying person's hand.*
3. *Be alert to the breathing.*
   If the person is short of breath, begin stroking the arm at the rate of breathing, then slow down. As you slow your stroke down, the breathing will also slow down and become the speed of your stroke.
4. *Be calm—the dying person may become agitated.*
5. *Talk slowly and quietly.*

There is also a quote from *Talking About Death Won't Kill You* that puts these thoughts in perspective: "A good death is for the dying and for the people who love them."

REFLECT

Questions to guide your reflection:

What kind of death is best for you?

What is a good death for you?

How are you prepared?

Who will be there to support you?

What does dignity mean to you?

Quotes to ponder:

"Life is not the way it is supposed to be .... It is the way it is! The way you cope with it is what makes the difference."

"In life you win .... In death you win."

"God chooses what we go through .... we choose how we go through it."

"Life is about celebrating the moment ... believing in dreams .... listening to your heart .... and enjoying the journey."

REACT

Activity	*Video: Creating a Good Death: Coping with Terminal Illness*
Instructions:	Show video: DVD – ABC News Nightline

Films for the Humanities and Sciences

1. During the film, have students write down any characteristics of a good death that they hear or observe.
2. Following the viewing of the film, write a composite list of the "Good Death" characteristics on the board.
3. Compare the film's list to the "Principles of a Good Death."
   Which ones were not in the film?
   Which ones were not on the "Principles of a Good Death" list?

Activity	*Poem: Do Not Stand By My Grave and Weep*

Instructions:
1. Time: end of class
2. Have students put heads down with eyes closed.
3. Read the poem aloud.
4. You are in a cemetery, imagine standing over a grave – maybe of a loved one or friend.
5. Pause 1 minute.

RECOMMENDED TERMS/ IMPORTANT PEOPLE/WEBSITES

Terms

Death rattle: A gurgling or rattling sound sometimes made in the throat of the
                             dying person, caused by the passage of the breath through the
                             accumulating mucus or fluid build-up in the back of the throat.

NOTES

Having to say good bye to my loved ones

Die in my home

Holding my mom/dad or wives hand

Talk about happy memories
One Last Kiss

V
Hospice...
"Comfort on a journey"

READ

One might ask the question, "What can you do for me?" Hospice might reply, "We want to help you live until you die." The goal of hospice is not to fight death, but to make the most of life, however much or little that is. This is accomplished by helping the patient, who has a limited time left to live, to be as comfortable as possible, in addition to helping the patient and the family find peace.

Where did hospice begin?

The term *hospice* (from the same linguistic root as the word, hospitality) can be traced back to medieval times when it referred to a place of shelter and rest for weary or ill travelers on a long journey. The name was first applied to specialized care for dying patients in 1967 by physician, Dame Cicely Saunders, who founded the first modern hospice, St. Christopher's Hospice, located in a residential suburb of London.

Saunders introduced the idea of specialized care for the dying to the United States during a 1963 visit to Yale University. Her lecture, given to medical students, nurses, social workers, and chaplains about the concept of holistic hospice care, included photos of terminally ill cancer patients and their families, showing the dramatic differences before and after symptom-control care. This lecture launched a chain of events which resulted in the development of hospice care as we know it today (National Hospice and Palliative Care Organization).

What is hospice?

Hospice is a holistic program of care and comfort for the terminally ill. One of the strengths of hospice care is that it uses an interdisciplinary approach in offering care to terminally ill patients and their families. The interdisciplinary team is comprised of a medical doctor who oversees patient care. In addition, there are nurses, social workers, chaplains, certified nurses' aides, and volunteers. These professionals and volunteers work together to care for the physical, social, emotional, and spiritual needs of patients and families. The care is tailored to each patient's needs. It is recognized, as in all good care, that the patient and family are treated as one unit. The main focus is for the patient to die as peacefully as possible.

Where is hospice?

Hospice programs are housed in office settings, and then the care is taken to wherever the patient lives. It may be in residential homes, nursing homes, and hospitals. There is an increasing number of "hospice houses" springing up. These are residential facilities for hospice patients to live out their last days in a home-like setting, receiving 24-hour care. Wherever a patient's home is, that is where hospice will meet and care for him or her.

How does one enter the hospice program?

To enter a hospice program as a patient, a physician must give the patient a prognosis of six months or less to live. Following this referral, usually a nurse and/or a social worker visits the patient and family to make an initial physical and/or psychosocial assessment. Anyone, birth to 100+ years of age, may qualify to receive hospice care.

Once the patient has been approved, the other team members contact the patient and family to visit and make their own assessments and plans of care. A patient may stay as a patient longer than six months, but there must be documentation that he or she is in a state of decline throughout the length of stay. In other words, a doctor can do another referral note for another 6 months. There are possibilities of someone relinquishing hospice care with improvement in his or her condition and illness, which is a hope for all.

How much does it cost?

This is a common question. It costs patients and families little, if any money at all. Medicare, Medicaid, and private insurances reimburse hospice for medical equipment, medications that are related to the patient's diagnosis, and for most of the professionals who make up the interdisciplinary team.

Why hospice?

One of the values of hospice and one of the incentives of its development is that it recognizes the suffering of both patient and family and takes an interdisciplinary approach to managing the suffering. Hospice highlights the many remedies, from counseling to spiritual care, from volunteers to grief support, alleviating that pain. Medications used may be for anxiety, nausea, drying the death rattle, or actual morphine for the pain. From pain medication to medical equipment, hospice provides comfort and support, twenty-four hours a day, seven days a week.

Because there are physical, emotional, social, and spiritual components to everyone, pain and suffering can affect the whole person. Since one of the goals of hospice is to keep patients pain free, this is accomplished with the interdisciplinary team addressing the whole person, including the family.

4 Levels of Treatment

Routine Home Care (*Intermittent*):	Patient care in the home, assisted living, or nursing home.
Respite Care:	Patient can be moved to a nursing home facility for 4-5 days. *(The patient may stay in the facility up to 5 days)* This my be due to the caregiver: 1. Being exhausted – the need for a break or some relief 2. Being ill 3. Needing to attend a graduation, wedding, or special event
In-Patient Care (*Crisis/Aggressive*):	If there is an issue of pain that cannot be controlled at home or in the facility, the patient can be admitted to the hospital or an "in-patient unit" for a short period of time for pain management.
Continuous Care (*Crisis/Aggressive*):	Patient's symptoms may be out of control and is in need of 24-hour care. A nurse is with the patient 24/7 working 8-hour shifts.

The "FINAL" Days: Signs and Symptoms that a patient is close to death
RESOURCE: Hospice and Palliative Nurses Association (HPNA)

As death nears, one may see the patient do any of the following:

Sleeps more
Speak to people not present
Talk about leaving or taking a trip or journey

Withdraw from people or have a little to say
Eat or drink less
Have trouble swallowing
Become more confused
Make moaning sounds
Lose control of urination and bowel movements
Have moist breathing or sound congested
Have changes in breathing patterns….such as long periods
without breathing followed by several quick deep breaths
Have blurred vision
Have less pain
Have cool feeling hand and arms or feet/legs
Turn blue around nose, mouth, fingers toes

What should be reported to the Hospice/Palliative Care Team?

Changes in the patient: restlessness – anxiety – breathing –
pain/discomfort?
Need for spiritual support or guidance for the patient or family?
Concerns that may need help from the social worker–
chaplain – other hospice team members?
Any religious – cultural – ethnic traditions….important to pa-
tient and family?

What can we do?

The hospice team will work with the patient to relieve symptoms and increase comfort.
The "GOAL" of the Hospice Team? …..……..
"Comfort for the patient and for the family!"

Allow the patient to sleep as much as they wish.
Include the children in the family in the death experience.
Turn the patient if it makes him/her more comfortable.
Moisten the patient's mouth with a moist washcloth or
*   cotton ball.*
If patient has a fever or is hot, apply a cool cloth to the forehead.
Give medications ordered by doctor to decrease anxiety –
*   restlessness – agitation – moist breathing.*
Write down what the patient says…messages may comfort
*   you later.*
Continue to talk clearly to the patient…….say the things you
*   need or want to say……the patient may be able to hear*
*   even when unable to respond (sense of hearing is the last*
*   to go).*
Keep light on in the room…patient cannot see well and may
*   be scared by darkness and shadows.*
Play the patient's favorite music softly.
Encourage visitors to talk directly to the patient…tell the
*   patient who you are.*

Keep things calm around the patient.
Open a window…use a fan…if the patient is having trouble
    breathing.
Touch and stay close to your loved one.

<u>At the time of death…what will Hospice want to know?</u>
 1. *Name of funeral home you will want to use?*
 2. *Whether the body will be embalmed or cremated?*
 3. *Names of family members to be contacted?*

<u>Perspective on hospice</u>

The hospice team members are very much aware that they witness sacred moments. Few people have the honor of sharing a moment of death, the moment of passing from this finite world that has held the patient's body. The journey of death is a type of labor, of giving birth to something new, and these nurses, chaplains, social workers, and aides are the midwives.

One highlight of hospice that sets it apart is the bereavement program. It is acknowledged that care for the patient and family does not end with the patient's death. For the family, often their greatest pain is just beginning. Their focus for months, and sometimes years, is caring for their loved one. From the point of death, their caregiving stops. The focus changes to the caregivers and their grief. Hospice stays in contact with bereaved families for thirteen months following the death. One of the ways they do this is by hosting grief support groups that are open not only to bereaved hospice families, but also to the community. Other ways hospice offers bereavement care is by sending cards to the family upon the first anniversary of their loved one's death and on the first birthday of their loved one following the death. If visits are needed for grief counseling, social workers and chaplains are available to the family.

Comfort on a journey

"Comfort" is the adjective that most describes hospice. Just as hospitals offer cures, and nursing homes give care, hospice offers comfort. The three Cs describing hospice are compassion, care, and comfort with "comfort" being the final destination.

Hospice strives to provide dignity and quality of life for the dying person. This may be seen as the final journey where one reflects on the past and present, and where hopes, dreams, faith and doubt are all held together. Hospice does not shy away from remaining at the side of the patient who struggles to thread these companions as part of a tapestry giving dimension to one person's life.

REFLECT

If you were told that you had six months to live:

*Where are the places you would go?

*With whom would you have a conversation?

*What would you talk about in your conversations?

- *Do you need reconciliation with someone?*
- *Have you lost touch with an old friend with whom you can reconnect?*
- *What would you tell your children?*

*Use your imagination and these questions to think of other reflections.

Quotes to ponder:

"When bad things happen.... what do good people do?"

"Run the bases for someone."

"How do you live the rest of your life in just a few days?"

"Death is what happens when we die."

"Live every day until you die."

REACT

Activity   *Hospice Presentation*
                      (if possible, include a promotional film about hospice)

Instructions: Invite a local hospice professional to speak to the class.
During the presentation, instruct students to take notes and answer the following questions:
1. List five professionals who make up the interdisciplinary team.
2. List three places where a hospice patient can be given care.
3. Describe three components of the bereavement program.
4. Of what age spans are hospice patients comprised?
5. Write a one-page reflection paper of your thoughts and feelings during the presentation. This may include memories you have of a death in your life, a personal experience with hospice, or simply your impressions. Remember, the instructions are to write your reflections, not a summary of the presentation.

Activity   *Speaker Notes*

Guest Speaker: Sonya Rawlings

Topic: **Feelings as you listen?**

The Goal of Hospice:

Organization designed to help people at the end of their life

Provide a plan

Misconceptions:

What is the "Team" approach and who makes up the team? ~~medical director, nurse and chaplain~~

Patient's Plan:

The team consists of: *Role on the Team:*
1. medical director
2. nurse
3. aids
4. chaplain
5.
6.
7.
8.

When is the team available?

24/7

What are the 3 C's for Hospice? comfort, care

   C: comfort
   C: care
   C: compassion

Where can Hospice take place?

What are the requirements to enter a Hospice Program?
   1.
   2.
   3.

Possibility of changing "DNR" to "AND"?

very likely

What is the age limit to use Hospice?

no limit

What are the 4 levels of Hospice care?
> *Least to most expensive (#3 & #4 are Most Aggressive)*
> 1. Routine Care *home care*
> 2. Respite Care: *a break*
> 3. In Patient Care: *in ~~~~~ small pain. Home to Hospice*
> 4. Continuous/Crisis Care: *sit by their bed 12 hours a day*

Any "Medications" used?

yes

Can a Hospice patient ever go off of Hospice?

as many times they want

What is the cost?

Medicare, Medicaid

What is the bereavement program?

emotional comfort for the ones who lost someone

How long does the bereavement period last?

Meeting "Grief Needs" of the Staff?

RECOMMENDED TERMS/ IMPORTANT PEOPLE/WEBSITES

Terms

Palliative care: (pronounced: pal-lee-uh-tiv)
The medical specialty of comprehensive care that focuses on the relief of pain, stress, and other debilitating symptoms of serious illness.
Palliative care is not dependent on prognosis and can be delivered at the same time as treatment that is meant to cure.
The goal is to relieve suffering and provide the best possible quality of life for patients and their families. Also known as comfort care.
HOSPICE is a type of palliative care.

Important people

Dr. Dame Cicely Saunders, the founder of the modern hospice movement.

Websites

National Hospice and Palliative Care Organization: www.nhpco.org

Center for the Advancement of Palliative Care: www.getpalliative.org

NOTES

VI
Listening and Good Manners at the End of Life…
"The gift of presence"

READ

Listening

Throughout our learning and talking about dying and death, the topic of listening is not to be omitted. Listening is one of the five senses that becomes a definite part of the end-of-life experience. *Listening is defined as "giving ear, hearing with thoughtful attention, paying attention to, or giving ear to conversation or music."* Listening is a skill that is used constantly until our death. We are told that hearing *is the last sense to leave our body before death occurs.* The dying person may possibly hear conversations taking place in the room during the time of dying. Whether it is listening to the patient, family, friends, or the physician, it is an act that demands our attention.

We listen to happy and sad times. We listen in an educational setting or in nature. We find ourselves surrounded by the loud noises of the busy day, and then we are ready to embrace the quiet, peaceful noises of the night. Whatever the time or setting, if the sound or subject is something in which we are interested, we will have our ears perked. Otherwise, we have a tendency to turn away and block out that sound; in other words, we have a deaf ear. Careful listening definitely has a place in a dying and death situation.

Hearing bad news about a loved one may send us into shock and we find that we may have missed important information from the medical professionals or others. Once the shock resides and we gain more clarity, we may then ask questions and hear what we need to hear. On the other hand, when we are reminiscing during our conversations with the dying or with family and friends, we are usually very interested in those memories and we listen more intently because we want to be included.

Whether we are listening to the wishes of the dying person or listening to the problems of a friend, it is tempting to give advice. In doing so, we could miss some important details of what that person wants to say by focusing on what we want to tell them rather than what they want or need to tell us. Being aware of our own needs during such an important time can ensure that we do not become an obstacle in meaningful conversations. Time may be a factor in giving advice too quickly, or in not having time to sit down and listen. Another factor may be one of interest—maybe we are simply not interested in the topic or do not know what to say. Each of these factors can interrupt the process of being a good listener.

Not interrupting the story or the important information being presented is difficult for some people. Some people want to automatically step in before the full story is told. When we are taught manners growing up, we have always been told "do not interrupt someone when he or she is talking." So why do we do this? We think we know the answer right away, want to finish the story or give advice. Perhaps we are simply very interested in the subject and want to have input.

Whatever the situation, being a good listener demonstrates respect and good manners. Regardless of where we are or what we are doing, whether we have the time, whether we are listening carefully or turn a deaf ear, whether we stay focused or interrupt with our own advice, the art of listening is a skill that we all can improve. It takes practice to become a good listener. Having strong listening skills can be used in everyday life from the time we are children until the end of our lives. It is a marvelous skill to acquire, and the better the listener, the better the communication one has with another person. To listen with intention and care is to express an act of love.

<u>Acts of Listening</u>

An Act of Compassion
A person enters the life of another person and experiences that life as that person does.

An Act of Empathy
A person has the ability to hear the feelings in another person's story without a judgmental reaction. A person has the ability to ask questions and relate to the feelings of that person. An

appropriate response to someone would begin with the phrase, "You feel..." For example, "You feel lost now that your mother is no longer with you."

An Act of Sympathy

A person can identify with another person's feelings, can give advice, and is able to express feelings for the other person. An appropriate response to someone would begin with the phrase, "I feel..." For example, "I feel sad to learn of the death of your mother."

"Listening Continuum"

This brings us to the question: How can you improve your listening? There is a sequence of progressions in "The Listening Continuum" that can assist us in developing stronger listening skills. Learning and practicing these actual steps will help us realize what is usually left out. There are six basic steps. Usually, a person begins listening with steps 4, 5, and 6. Are good at giving reassurance while analyzing and giving advice, but now we need to practice the first three steps.

*Steps in Good Listening–The Listening Continuum**

1.	Reflection of Feelings:	Giving descriptive adjectives back to the person on "how they feel."
2.	Content:	Repeating steps, order, progression, or sequence of events … "How to…"
3.	Questions:	Use open-ended questions. Try to get information; do not use "yes/no/why" type questions.
4.	Reassurance:	Best to give in small doses: "It will be ok…" "It will be over…" "You will be able to…"
5.	Diagnose and Analyze:	Figuring out the problem. Use of "I" will make the person feel better. "I see what is going on"…
6.	Advice:	Advising—people want to fix things— choices. Person will not hear advice if said at the beginning. It is not unusual that by the time you get to this step, the person may have solved his or her own problem

Good manners

Manners is defined as *"a social conduct or rules of conduct as shown in a prevalent custom, a characteristic or customary mode of acting, kind, fashionable, a method of artistic presentation."* Most of us were

*"Listening Continuum" by Dr. Robert D. Myrick. Copyright by Dr. Robert D. Myrick. Reprinted with permission of the author.

taught good manners and proper etiquette as we grew up, and we were expected to use them in public places as well as at home. The simple words of "please" and "thank you" always preceded the request, and it seemed to have brought or helped us receive whatever we were seeking. Not only words were expected, but also actions. Respect for our elders included opening doors, always giving the titles of "Mr." or "Mrs." (especially in certain parts of the country), and possibly extending a handshake. Whether it is verbal or nonverbal, good manners still need to be at the top of the list of our conduct.

The consideration in the use of manners also applies to end of life. But what do we do in an emotional and stressful situation? The environment is sensitive, and the dying person may even be in a coma or barely able to talk. How do we use good manners in an end-of-life situation and know that the dying person and his or her family is respected? We must show that respect, whether it be for a child or adult, relative or friend. The time of listening and saying our good-byes to the ones we love is most difficult. Being able to say and do the appropriate things during this difficult time can bring a necessary calmness. This type of atmosphere will allow cherished moments to become cherished memories.

What can we do to exhibit good manners with the dying person?

The 10 "be" manners:

• Be there	A visit does not have to be long. A dying person may want to have others in the room… remember the fear of being lonely.
• Be a giver	Take a vase of fresh flowers, a frozen meal, a journal, a book, or a card.
• Be supportive	Let the dying person know you are there for him, that you support his wishes and decisions.
• Be helpful	Ask what you can do…run errands, go to the store, wash the dishes, write a thank you note, or take care of a pet. There is always something that needs to be done.
• Be a writer	Write a letter or note to the family or patient—this may become a keepsake for the family later on.
• Be at ease	Be yourself, be natural, let life go on in a normal way. The person will know your tone of voice, so talk like you always do.
• Be a listener	Use that sense of hearing…remember to reflect adjectives, provide

	information, ask questions to get information and reassure.
• Be honest	Getting information may be useful at a later time.
	Say what you need to say-- "I don't know what to say...," "I can't imagine how you feel...," "Tell me what I can do to help..." "I will miss you..." "I love you, too."
• Be calm	The person may get angry; that is ok. You can say, "I don't blame you for being angry." The person may react with hard scribbling or hitting a pillow; that is ok.
• Be normal with the person	Treat the dying person like a normal person. An adult does not like being treated like a child.

What about good manners when we observe a funeral taking place?

1. We need to act with reverence.
2. If we are driving and observe a motorcade leaving a funeral home to proceed to the cemetery, we should slow down, pull over to the side, and stop. This shows respect for the person who has died.

What about good manners when we attend a funeral and interment?

1. Dress respectfully.
2. Enter the funeral home quietly and reverently.
3. Do not interrupt the conversation or service.
4. Pay respect to the family, but do not keep them in conversation for a lengthy time.
5. If following in the motorcade, drive slowly, turn on lights, and keep position in line following the police escort directions.
6. When attending the burial or interment, silence is expected.

Summary

Being a good listener and expressing good manners are essential elements in an end-of-life experience.
Neither of these comes easily in a time of emotion and stress.
It takes everyday practice for these skills to become a natural process.
Demonstrating good manners, including being a good listener, benefits all aspects and stages throughout our lifetime... as a child, a student, a husband or wife, a parent, an employee, an employer, and in retirement.
Listening and good manners...the gift of presence.

REFLECT

Questions to help guide your reflection:

*List three places that would be good to have a listening conversation with a friend.

*Describe three qualities that you possess that will enhance your listening skills.

*Which part of the listening continuum is most difficult for you?

*Which part of the listening continuum is easiest for you?

*How often do you include "thank you" and "please" in your manners?

*Who was most influential in your life regarding your manners and why?

*What would be the first thing that you would do when visiting a dying person?

*Reflect on the act of silence as a skill and a gift in the presence of the dying.

Quotes to ponder:

"The saddest words are those that are unspoken."

"You never know what a day may bring?"

REACT

Activity   *Listening in Threes*

Instructions: 1. Divide the class into groups of three.
2. Number each person in the group #1, # 2, #3
3. There will be three different people for each action:
   The storyteller—the listener—and the monitor who listens for correctness in the listener's responses
4. Action #1: Reflection of Feelings
   a. Have #1 tell #2 a story about "how to get to a certain place"
   b. #1 talks for one minute; #2 can only reflect feelings, #3 monitors.
5. Action #2: Reflection of Content
   a. Have #2 tell #3 something that they do very well that has an order of steps to it:
   Examples: bake a cake, change the oil, throw a ball.
   b. #2 talks for 1 ½ minutes; #3 can reflect feelings and content; #1 monitors.
6. Action #3: Questions?
   a. Have #3 tell #1 something about the upcoming holidays.
   b. #3 talks for 2 minutes; #1 can reflect feelings, content, and ask open-ended questions; #2 monitors.

7. Action #4: Fish Bowl
   a. Choose #1, #2, or #3 to tell the story:
      Topics: Bullying – parent to teacher
                  Stress of family and job – teacher to teacher
                  Cell-phone generation – friend to friend
   b. Then select one of the other numbers to listen.
   c. The last number is the monitor.
   d. Storyteller has 5 minutes to tell story; listener includes all
      six parts of the Listening Continuum; last number monitors.
8. Wrap up: include reassuring, analyzing, and advising.
   a. What was the most difficult part for you?
   b. Which was the easiest part?
   c. How often did the monitors have to interrupt?
   d. How did your listening skills improve?

Activity   ***Empty Chair***

Instructions: Need: Two empty chairs facing each other
1. Have two volunteers come to the front and sit in the chairs.
2. One volunteer will be the listener. The other volunteer will be the storyteller.
3. Pick one of the following scenarios:
Note: These scenarios can be changed to fit your audience.

Scenario A
You have asked a friend if he or she has a minute or two to give you some advice about your roommate problems. Your roommate is stealing food from you, and you have also been missing some money. It is late in the semester to be finding other housing, but you are really frustrated by the situation. You are also overwhelmed by projects, finals, and grade expectations.

Scenario B
You have asked your friend if he or she could recommend a good doctor because you are having lots of trouble with your stomach and with really bad headaches. You wake some mornings with your stomach burning and some foods are really upsetting to your system. The headaches are worse when you read, and you have major reading assignments due within the next month.

Scenario C
You have asked your friend for some advice about your boy/girl friend situation. This relationship has been going on for six months, and you enjoy being with this person, but he or she wants a more serious commitment from you...an exclusive relationship. You do not feel quite ready for an exclusive relationship right now. You wonder how to talk to him or her about it and are looking to your friend to help you out.

RECOMMENDED TERMS/ IMPORTANT PEOPLE/WEBSITES

Terms

Compassion:
Sympathetic consciousness to others' distress together with a desire to alleviate that distress.

Continuum:
An uninterrupted ordered sequence, continuity.

Empathy:
The capacity for participation in another's feelings or ideas.

Interment:
The burial of a corpse, usually accompanied by a funeral ceremony.

Listening:
Giving ear, hearing with thoughtful attention, paying attention to, or giving ear to conversation or music.

Manners:
A social conduct or rules of conduct as shown in a prevalent custom, a characteristic or customary mode of acting, kind, fashionable, a method of artistic presentation.

Sympathy:
Feeling of loyalty; tendency to favor or support; inclination to feel or think alike; emotional or intellectual accord.

Important people

Dr. Robert Myrick
University of Florida
Developed "The Listening Continuum"

NOTES

VII
Physicians and Medical Choices…

"Choices-Choices…Decisions-Decisions"

READ

Our lives are comprised of decision-making. We choose what to eat for breakfast; we choose what university to attend; we choose whether or not to marry; we choose professions and we choose places to retire.

Similarly, at the end of our lives, we have choices and so we have decisions to make. We will have choices about the medical professionals we want to accompany us. We will be asked to consider if we want a local medical team or if we want to go out of town. We will have choices about whether or not to have treatment for our disease. If we choose to be treated, then we will have decisions to make about the type of treatment we want and how long we want to have it. Other questions might be, do we want to stay at home, or do we want to enter a medical facility?

It is not too early to begin considering these questions. Some of these choices can be pondered even when we are young adults. Others will be considered as we age or when we are diagnosed with a disease. Regardless, to give thought to our options is to choose a healthy and positive way to live.

In order to guide us in our decisions, we ask questions and observe others. We may listen to professionals and have conversations with family and friends who have had similar experiences. When making decisions about which medical professionals we want to advise and care for us, it is important that we discuss our situation with more than one physician or medical team. Being patient throughout our experiences can help us have a sense of peace that we are making the right decision.

With every decision that we make regarding how to live our final days, we gain something and we give up something. If we choose treatment that will prolong our life, sometimes that means to choose a quality of life that is not optimal due to possible side effects of the treatment. It is easy to make choices based on what we think others want us to do. If we can get away from feeling guilty about the choices we make, we can look at the issues in a different light. We know that making these decisions may not be black and white, but a shade of gray. It is easy to wait too long in this difficult process. Nature will take its course. We are all born and we will all die. We just do not know when. With respect for nature and the circle of life, may our decision-making be seen as acts of love for ourselves and for our loved ones. Let's look at some of the medical choices we will be faced with to ensure that we have the kind of life we want.

Physicians

We all will have to choose a doctor. Whether it is a general practitioner or a specialist, at some point we will need their expertise. How is a doctor chosen? We will begin with information on training and professional practice.

<u>Training and professional practice</u>
The goal of the physician: to help cure people.
Usually when a person is interested in becoming a professional in the medical field, he or she wants to help people in some way.

Medical school: how long is the physician's training?
Following graduation from a four-year college or university where the person received a degree that fulfills the medical school qualifications, that person has to be accepted into a specific medical school. Applying to a medical school is a tedious process during the last two years of undergraduate work, including taking medical school entrance examinations. Once a person is accepted, then the training begins:

1st–2nd years: *Technical learning, biological facts, memorizing, passing tests*
3rd year: *Begin dealing with humans*
4th year: *More extensive work with patients*

Residency:	*On the job experience; seeking a specialized field. This training may take three to five years.*
Taking the Hippocratic Oath:	*The oath is lengthy, but basically says to look to cure and at the minimum to do no harm, treating to prevent disease while respecting the privacy and confidentiality of patients.*

Do medical schools prepare physicians to deal with death?

Most medical schools offer end-of-life training within another course rather than as an individual course designated specifically for dying and death. Approximately 40 percent of medical students have never heard a physician talk about dying. This lack of training presents itself later when working with patients. Often a physician, and even the nursing profession, will avoid telling the truth to the dying patient or will not talk about death due to their taken oath "to cure," or due to their own fear of death. They may even justify not talking about death indicating that the patient was not willing to talk about end of life. One can see this practice in a medical office as well as in a hospital setting.

What outside pressures can a physician face in the profession?
1. Lawsuits
2. Research: keeping up-to-date in the chosen field
3. Innovative treatments
4. Managed care: See a certain number of patients in a certain amount of time
5. Time
   a. Time for talking with patients
   b. Time to make hospital rounds
      (Note: There is a new trend to have "hospitalists" in hospitals. This physician sees the patients and then acts as a liaison between the patient and his or her private physician. This has helped to offer a solution to the use of time.)
6. Personal beliefs about death
7. Personal peer pressure within the profession
8. Budget; money
9. Tenure
10. Media
11. Receiving awards

What do physicians need to learn?
1. How to relay bad news
   a. Factors that influence conversation: age, sex, religion, education, family, professional peer pressure.
   b. Most people want to be told if they have a life-threatening illness.
   c. The most difficult questions to answer will be: HOW and WHEN?
      According to Dr. Ronald Wilson, a nephrologist in Waco, Texas, there is no absolute answer to these questions, but a

physician needs to communicate to the patient and the family that he or she is providing his or her best estimate of the patient's condition and that the human body may not respond as expected. When death occurs outside the predicted time frame, a physician needs to be sensitive that family members may lose faith and confidence in him or her.

2. How to have clear communication in talking with patients:
   a. Listen with eyes and ears.
   b. Positive attitudes affect ultimate outcomes and the healing system.
   c. Negative attitudes may reflect despondency and despair.
3. How to handle responses: anger and denial from patients.
4. How to observe body language: gestures, uneasiness, anxiety.
5. How to be honest and truthful in diagnosis.
6. How to initiate discussion of care.
7. How to include patient's desires, too—it is a shared decision— this is crucial!
8. How to acknowledge limits of medicine.
9. How to talk about financial issues: Is the family supportive in all areas?
   Does the medical system accommodate the patient's preference?
10. How to become familiar with the laws.
11. How to be familiar with palliative care.

What are the dynamics of death for a physician? Who is involved?

1. Patient
2. Family and friends
3. Medical staff

10 Tips on how to deliver bad news to a patient

1. *Prepare yourself to feel badly.*
   No matter how people feel before they hear bad news, they always feel worse afterwards.
2. *Set the context.*
   Give the person time to prepare themselves.
3. *Deliver the bad news clearly and unequivocally.*
   Softening the blow by using jargon is powerful, but detrimental. It delays the patient's understanding of the truth and can promote denial.
4. *Stop!*
   Let the person react. Then your job is to respond to their reaction and help them through it. Because of shock, they will not hear your explanation.
5. *Ask for questions.*
   Once the reaction has run its course, ask for questions.
   Answer honestly and directly.
6. *They may not ask questions, but sometimes they do.*
   They may ask the question you dread the most… "Is this terminal?" Tell them the truth… "Nothing is certain."

7. *Never destroy hope!*
   Quality of life becomes important. Think carefully before you speak. Try not to enable false hope. What you don't say allows people to continue to hope.

8. *Express your commitment of support.*
   Make it a point to say..."I will not abandon you." This provides some type of relief and lets the patient know there is someone in a position of authority who genuinely cares. You can also add... "I will not let you suffer."

9. *Make a plan!*
   Give patients a series of instructions. Tell them:
   1. Write down any questions you may have.
   2. Tell your family.
      Do know that some patients may not want family to know the news. Death with secrets often leaves wounds in survivors that never heal.
   3. Prepare yourself for what comes next. It may be testing or treatment or both or neither.

10. *Follow up!*
    Always talk with the person within a week. This can be done in person or by a phone call. Time will often allow shock to soften in coming to terms with the news. The patient will begin to take action to deal with it.

Patients and families remember how bad news is delivered! They will remember the doctor's words, how the doctor looked, and whether they seemed to care. Before you enter that door to deliver bad news, *PAUSE!* Remember, you are about to change someone's life!

What are the problems physicians face in medical treatment for patients?
1. Cost of the treatment.
2. Income loss for the patient due to not being able to work.
3. Recognition that death is evitable—human cells are programmed genetically to die (*apoptosis*).
4. Paranoia or prejudice: suspicion, not trusting, anger, lawsuits.
5. Technology is driving the cost up.

How does a physician determine if a patient is brain dead?
Following are some tests used to clinically determine if a person is brain dead.
1. **Cold Water Caloric:**
   Procedure: Injecting cold water into the ear.
   This stimulates the vestibular system—rapid eye movement.
   If there is eye movement, the person is still alive.
2. **EEG:**
   Should have no electrical activity (flatline). There are usually two consecutive tests 24 hours apart for the purpose of organ donation.

3. *No blood flow to brain:*
Includes nuclear medicine brain scan, transcranial doppler sonography, and arteriogram.

4. *Apnea test:*
Test to measure the amount of CO_2. The respirator is turned off. The patient's chest is observed for 1–2 minutes watching for signs of spontaneous breathing. After 10 minutes, the amount of CO_2 is measured.

If the pCO_2 (partial pressure arterial carbon dioxide) is greater than or equal to 60 mm Hg (mercury) or the pCO_2 increase is > 20 mm Hg over the baseline normal pCO_2, the apnea test is positive, supporting the clinical diagnosis of brain death.

A few terms that you may hear a physician use:

Brain dead: Brain does not function.
Causes: head injury, brain tumor, drugs, stroke, anoxic brain injury.
Machines and medications can be used to maintain heart rate and blood oxygen levels.

Clinical death:

Absence of pulse, respiration, and/or blood pressure, cold, mottled.

Definitions:

Pulse:	Heart beats—use EKG, stethoscope, or feel carotid/radial artery.
Respiration:	Breaths—use stethoscope or fog on a mirror.
Blood Pressure:	Pressure of blood as it passes through arteries—use a blood pressure cuff.

Exceptions to the clinical death:

Hypothermia:	Frozen—must warm up the body before pronouncing the death.
Dive Reflex:	Surfacing too quickly from deep water.
Certain drug overdoses mimic death:	Downers and barbiturates.
Neurological:	Brain death, but patient has a pulse and blood pressure. Causes: head trauma or medical hemorrhage

Treatment for clinical death exceptions:
Maintain pulse, blood pressure, respiration using technology.

Coma: A very deep sleep; seems like heavy anesthesia. A prolonged state of deep unconsciousness.

✳ Frederick's Spot: A small red spot on one side of the lower back (hip) that is in the shape of a butterfly. This is a symbol that the dying process has begun. This butterfly symbol is not found on everyone who is in the process of dying.

Rigor Mortis: Stiffness of the body following death; usually occurs several hours following the death.

Persistent Vegetative State: A twilight zone between life and death. A medical condition in which a patient, who shows no response to stimuli, has severe brain damage and as a result is unable to stay alive without the aid of a life-support system.

<u>What are possible changes and signs that death is occurring?</u>

The "Dying Experience" is unique in its own way and time!

1–3 Months prior to death:

1. Withdrawal or separation from the world and then from people.
2. Increase in sleep (*more asleep than awake*) due to changes taking place on the inside of body.
3. Staying in bed.
4. Communicating less.
5. "Touch" takes on new meaning.
6. Going inside self.
7. Decrease in food intake or eating may stop. One does not need physical energy anymore, but the "spiritual energy" will be the sustainer. (*No cravings - prefer liquids-meat will go 1st – vegetables and soft foods, next*)

1–2 Weeks prior to death:

1. Disorientation
   a. Sleeping most of the time.
   b. Thinking becomes confused.
   c. Talking about the past or with people who have died.
   d. Agitation may occur.
   e. Picking at clothes.
2. Physical signs:
   a. Decrease in blood pressure.
   b. Increase or decrease in pulse beat.
   c. Body temperature may include fever or be hot and cold.
   d. Increased perspiration and clamminess.
   e. Skin color may be flushed with a blue or pale yellow color.
   f. Nail beds, hands, and feet will turn pale and bluish due to the heart slowing down.

g. Breathing changes can increase or decrease. May puff or blow on lips on exhaling.

h. Congestion with possible "death rattle" may be present or the next minute not be present.

i. Sleeping most of the time, but will respond.

j. Body may be in a state of feeling tired and heavy.

h. Eating will stop or may include very little fluids.

Days to hours prior to death:

1. The signs for 1-2 week prior to death become more intense.
2. There may be a surge in energy.
   a. May seem alert when earlier there was disorientation.
   b. A favorite meal may be requested when nothing had been eaten for days.
   c. Might visit with relatives when they had not wanted to be with anyone.
   d. Spiritual energy needed to transition to the next world is apparent.
   e. Physical expression is used.
3. Restlessness may increase due to lack of oxygen in the blood.
4. May become non-responsive and unable to respond to the environment.
5. Physical signs:
   a. Breathing patterns become slower and irregular or may stop for 15 to 30-45 seconds at a time.
   b. Pulse becomes very weak and hard to find.
   c. Congestion may become loud. Laying on one's side may help.
   d. Decrease in blood pressure.
   e. Eyes will become glassy and teary, may be half open, but unable to see.
   f. Feet and hands turn purple.
   g. Knees, elbows, underarms, legs, back, and buttocks will become blotchy.
   h. Decrease in urine output.
   i. May wet or stool in the bed.

Minutes before death:

1. Breathing will feel like "fish out of water."
2. Cannot be awakened.

How we approach death depends on:

1. Our fear of life.
2. Our participation in life.
3. Our willingness to "let go of the known" to venture into a new life.

✻ 2 Factors in our resistance in meeting death:
1. Fear.
2. Unfinished business.

When is separation complete?
When breathing stops.
There may be 1 or 2 long spaced breaths.
The physical body is empty and the "owner is no longer in need of the vehicle."
They have entered a new life!

Physicians are faced with daily pressures. Not only do doctors have to possess the knowledge and expertise in the medical profession, but they must be able to work with all kinds of people in all kinds of situations, which will require other professional skills of the helping professions. The goal of helping people goes beyond medicine. They are "people persons" striving to make a person healthy in a positive way acknowledging not only physical needs, but meeting the psychological need of support.

What about the patient and physician?
As a patient or caregiver, we…
1. Must trust him or her.
2. Want him or her to make us feel safe.
3. Usually do not want him or her to leave the room.
4. Put him or her in charge.
5. Let him or her guide our care, hope, and responses.

What do we need to consider when choosing a physician?
We need a doctor who…
1. Fits our need.
2. We can trust and respect.
3. We can talk to openly and honestly.
4. We can shape a relationship with for most of our life; grow together.
5. Will allow us to be part of the final act; shared decision-making.
6. Can share your pain.
7. Can sit down with the family.
8. Knows care in all settings; experience.
9. Will understand our financial concerns.

So what lessons have physicians learned about dying?
Dr. Atul Gawande, a cancer surgeon and New York author, realized that he and other doctors did not know how to talk about dying. Mortality was something that was not taught or talked about so it was just eliminated from conversation. He interviewed more than 200 people

on the topics of aging, living with terminal illness, and dying. From the interviews, Dr. Gawande concluded nine lessons on what doctor's have really learned about dying:

- *What is death?*
- *The best way to talk about dying is to talk about living...life is a prize.*
- *Less medicine does not always mean less life.*
- *Talking about death is a skill.*
- *The nearer you think you are to death, the more your priorities change.*
- *The dependent want to be independent.*
- *Nursing homes are some of the saddest, most innovative places in the world.*
- *One problem with old age is that nursing homes market themselves to the young, not to the old.*
- *Where we die is changing... fast!*

Ezra Klein, Editor in Chief for Vox Media, wrote an article expressing his fear of death. As he interviewed Dr. Gawande about his nine lessons learned, Ezra Klein began to realize that most everyone has difficulty in talking about death. Using the basic science definition, Dr. Gawande believes death occurs when oxygen is no longer provided to the brain. In discussing death, he stressed that it is more important to talk about "living" life rather than "extending" life in a limited capacity. It should be considered that the use of less aggressive medical interventions at the end of life means more life and less pain. When a physician masters the skill of talking about dying, they should be praised and rewarded just as they are for their skills as a physician or surgeon. Dr. Gawande observed when young people know death is near, their priorities shift to a deeper relationship with family. Several months following death, that same generation will revert to seeking and achieving. In comparison, older adults recognize how fragile life is and will become focused on being connected to family and a few close friends. Dr. Gawande's interview revealed that "seniors" want to keep their independence by living close to family at an "intimate distance," but we know that living alone may require a need for help and dependence on others. Nursing homes have traditionally created a sad environment and they continue to market their services to the younger caregivers rather than the prospective senior residents. It is comforting to know that recent innovations in nursing facilities include transition to a more "home" living environment rather than an "institutional" model. The final idea that Dr. Gawande provided is the fact that where we die is changing at a rapid pace. We expect to have some control over our quality of life at the end of life and hospice has definitely entered the picture as a major consideration. In conclusion,

Ezra Klein's article and Dr. Gawande's lessons provide a positive perspective on death and dying.

Medical choices

We have provided some basic background information on physicians, what is involved in their professional practice, and what our possible choices are when considering a physician for our medical care. We do know that sooner or later we will be confronted with medical decisions that our physicians will need to know during our lifetime. Becoming familiar with the possible facilities, understanding the triangle of healthcare and new terms, knowing the approximate cost involved and the questions to ask will all provide some basic guidelines that will help us in making our decisions. We must reflect on our fears and the quality of life we want. All of this will affect what we want to do and the choices we make. How do we want to live? What do we want at the end-of-life? What do we not want at the end of life?

<u>What are the choices for facilities?</u>
We call them the three Cs:

Hospitals:	*CURE*
Nursing homes:	*CARE*
Hospice:	*COMFORT*

We have learned that most of us want to be at home when we die. One may choose to be in a hospital, or one may decide it is time to be in an assisted living facility. Remember, hospice can take place in hospitals, nursing homes, assisted living residences, special facilities like an Alzheimer's facility, or at home. It is one's individual choice!

<u>What is the triangle of healthcare and what are the new terms you will see?</u>
A triangle has three sides. So in healthcare, we need to be aware that there are three parts involved:

the patient—the physicians/staff—the medical care/institutions

All of these contribute to overall healthcare. Some of the new terms that you will see in insurance, prescriptions, and medical documents are the following:

Medical care/Institutions will be referred to as:	*"Products"*
Physicians/Staff will be called:	*"Provider"*
Patients will be called:	*"Consumer"*

What about the cost?

These are approximate costs and can be expected to increase. Medical costs will affect what choices we have and the decisions we make.

ICU:	Day:	$1500 +
	6 months:	$500,000 +
Dialysis Machine:	$25,000 + per patient	

It is imperative that we ask ourselves:
How much money do I have?
Do I have insurance?
Will my insurance cover the cost?
How much will the insurance cover?
Am I eligible for government programs such as Medicare or Medicaid?
How much do I want to spend?
We need to remember....It is our choice!

Other questions to ask ourselves:

1. Where do I want to spend my last days?
2. Who do I want to care for me?
3. Would I rather have access to medical technologies in a hospital?
   Questions we ask about the machines:
   a. What is life-support?
   b. What does it do?
   c. What does it look like?
   d. What is so horrible about it?
   e. What do we give up if we refuse it?
4. Would hospice be my choice?
5. What do I want to be told?
   a. Most people want to be told it is a life-threatening illness.
   b. Most people want to know HOW and WHEN death will occur.
      These are the most difficult questions to answer! We just do not know!

When is it more difficult to stop treatment?

It is more difficult to stop treatment after the treatment has already been administered.

What are the most common fears about dying?

Remember, there are *two common fears* a person has about dying:
1. He or she does not want to be alone.
2. He or she does not want to be in pain.

<u>Remember the Quality of Life?</u>

In Chapter II, we learned that the *"quality of life is the balance of life and quality together. It is a yardstick that measures the outcome of one's healthcare and the resources that provide better health for an individual. It is the adjusted life years that help us live longer."* Remember, you want to ask yourself: What is my quality of life? How do I want to live my life? It is your choice!

Now that we have some information that helps lay a foundation for making decisions, we can look a little deeper into the quality of life that we want in death. Following is a list of possible choices that one can consider when completing important end-of-life legal documents *(see Chapter VIII Legal Issues)*. Discussion of each choice will follow the list.

<u>End-of-Life Choices</u>

Here are some choices that will be discussed:
1. Organ donation
2. CMO
3. DNR
4. Hydration
5. Life support
6. Nutrition

1. Donation: The Gift of Life

Let me tell you a special story...

My name is Leigh Kackley and I received a new liver when I was 40 years old. I was diagnosed with a liver disease called primary sclerosing cholangitis when I was 18. It is a disease that causes the bile ducts throughout the liver to become enlarged and scarred. It is progressive and chronic. I lived with the disease 20 years before needing my liver transplant.

I was on the national wait list two years before receiving my new liver. I became extremely fatigued and found myself limiting my activities after work and on the weekends. I also became so jaundiced a friend started calling me "Daisy." I was transplanted at Baylor Medical Center in Dallas, Texas, in November 2002.

My donor was a 16-year-old young man. Not a day goes by that I am not astutely aware that I live because he did not. It is my desire to meet his family, hug them, and tell them how much I appreciate their choosing to give the gift of life.

Life after transplant has been sweet. I have changed jobs, completed a master's degree, and am going to begin work on my doctoral degree this coming fall. I would not have been able to do these things without my liver transplant. I am indeed privileged and blessed to live life this side of transplant.

Organ donation is universal. There is a definite need for it. Every day, the list of people who need organs gets longer and longer. Yes, it is a bittersweet situation—giving up a life in order to help save a life. Yet, knowing that a loved one helped to save another life can provide some comfort to a family. Through organ, eye, and tissue transplant, we have the opportunity to offer patients a new lease on life. The transplant recipient has another chance to be healthy, productive, and live a normal life while sharing that new life with family and friends. Who knows, that new life may help to save future generations. We do have the power to change someone else's world by being a donor.

Following is information that will support organ donation, answer any possible questions on being a donor or recipient, and provide information to those who may want to consider organ donation in their legal documents. What an act of kindness it would be to be an organ donor!

Following is information for the universal organizations as well as for the State of Texas:

1. <u>Organ Procurement Organization (OPO)</u>*
   There are 58 federal organ procurement organizations in the United States Regulations and policies are set by the United Network for Organ Sharing.
2. <u>The Organ Procurement and Transplantation Network (OPTN)</u>
   <u>United Network for Organ Sharing (UNOS)</u>
   1. Federal organization that maintains the National Patient Wait List.
   2. Computerized network of all patients waiting on an organ.
   3. Works with organ procurement organizations to match organs with recipients.
3. <u>Texas Organ Sharing Alliance (TOSA)</u>
   1. The organ procurement organizations for Texas
      a. There are 3 organ procurement organizations in Texas out of the 58 in the United States.
      b. TOSA is one of the three in Texas.
   2. It educates the public about organ donation and transplantation.
   3. It talks to families about donating a loved one's organs, acting as the liaison.
   4. It is the liaison between the donor family and the transplant recipient.
      <u>*Note on the team approach*</u>:
      The team works in pairs. Keeping privacy on both sides is a must!
      *The recipient will not know the donor unless the donor family agrees.
      Both sides must agree to correspond with each other.
   5. The team calls the National Donor Hotline.

*From "Donors Wanted: Navigating the Path to Organ and Tissue Donation" by Gina Comparini. http://journalism.berkeley.edu/projects/transplant/opo.html. Copyright © 2003 by Gina Comparini. Revised 2010. Reprinted with permission.

<u>A few facts:</u>

Shortage of donors: There are not enough organs to meet the demand.
2% will die on a ventilator.
1% of that 2% will have agreed to donate.
The sickest gets the organ first; the one with the most emergency.
80% are waiting for an organ.
20% receive the transplant.
In Texas alone, there are more than 8,000 people on the waiting list.

<u>What organs and tissues can be donated?</u>

Eight Organs: Liver, pancreas, two lungs, heart, two kidneys, small intestines

Tissues: Skin, heart valves, ligaments, tendons, cartilage, eyes

<u>What are medical conditions that rule out organ donation?</u>

1. HIV
2. Actively spreading cancer
3. Certain severe infections – determined by the OPTN

<u>Who can donate?</u>

1. Everyone has the potential to be an organ donor.
2. There is no age requirement: Babies to seniors can donate.
3. People with illnesses can donate organs that are not affected by the illness.

<u>What are the requirements to be a donor?</u>

1. Must die in a hospital: Only 2 percent die in a hospital on a ventilator.
2. Must be on a respirator; this keeps the organ alive (exception: tissues and eyes).
3. Must be declared brain dead.
4. Cardiac death: Organ donation occurs when the family chooses to take a loved one off of life support for reasons entirely apart from organ donation.

<u>Is there a law?</u>

It is against the law to buy or pay for an organ.

<u>A possible scenario for organ donation—How does it work?</u>

1. Person's death is imminent – hospital staff contacts the local OPO.
2. Then phone calls begin between the hospital, the OPO, and possibly a tissue bank.
3. When OPO receives the referral, they collect information about the patient to determine their suitability as a possible organ and tissue donor.
   Information will include:
   a. Age
   b. Medical and social history
   c. Any wishes the patient may have expressed in Advanced Directives

4. Based on the above information, the OPO accepts the patient as a referral.
5. The following is considered:
   a. If the patient has been *declared brain dead*, the OPO sends a Transplant Coordinator to the hospital to meet with the family and assist with clinical management of the donor.
   b. If the *diagnosis of brain dead has not been made*, the OPO simply stays in contact with the hospital staff and receives periodic updates on the patient's condition.
6. Once the patient has been declared brain dead, the OPO sends a Transplant Coordinator to the hospital for an in-depth evaluation of the patient to determine donor suitability. This includes examination of patient and the medical records.
7. If the patient is suitable for donation, the OPO approaches the family for consent. These individuals are trained to assist families with any cultural or religious questions about the donation process. Some states have a donor registry that the OPO will consult.
8. Does the family consent?
   a. ***If family declines: the process stops here!***
   b. *If the OPO receives **consent** and organs are viable for transplant, the process continues…
9. The OPO's placement department requests a list of compatible patients from UNOS.
10. After the family gives their consent, they usually make a final visit to their loved one and then leave the hospital.
11. While potential recipients are being located, the brain-dead donor is on a ventilator to preserve the body. Drugs and medications maintain blood pressure and body functions.
12. When organ recovery is complete, the Transplant Coordinator contacts the family and the body is ready to be transferred to the mortuary.
13. When the OPO placement coordinator identifies a recipient through UNOS, the donor's medical information is transmitted to the transplant coordinator or surgeon who is treating the patient who is waiting for a transplant.
14. They have one hour to accept or decline the organ based on the suitability of the organ and the intended recipient's current medical condition.
15. If the organ is not suited for the first patient, then the next patient on the list is offered the organ.
16. This process continues until all the organs are accepted.
17. Then the focus turns to the organ recovery:
    a. An operating room time is scheduled for organ recovery.
    b. The OPO Transplant Coordinator works with the hospital staff to maintain the organs until the transplant surgeons arrive to recover the organs.
    c. An OPO surgical coordinator and the transplant surgeons recover the organs.

     d. After the organ is recovered, the transplant surgeons return to their respective transplant centers where their patient(s) are waiting to undergo surgery.
18. The Transplant Coordinator stays with the donor and follows the body to the morgue.

Where do organs go?
All organs are allocated first locally with the OPO working with the transplant centers in their region. If there are no acceptances in the local region, then the allocation can expand to other outside areas.

What happens when you are in need of a transplant?
1. First, a committee decides whether or not you get on the recipient list. They consider your disease, how sick you are, and how bad your disease gets.
2. When the recipient gets to that "bad" point, they are told to be ready, they might receive that important call.
3. The recipient receives that call.
4. The recipient goes to transplant hospital as quickly as possible. The hospital will give a certain amount of time for the recipient to arrive at the hospital.
5. The recipient is met by hospital staff, registered as a patient, and goes directly to surgery for the organ transplant.

I know there are myths ... What are they?
1. The doctor won't try to keep me alive.
   Answer: NO, one must be brain dead.
2. If I designate that I want to be a donor, the hospital staff may not work to save me; they want my organs.
   Answer: NO, the hospital has no control, only the procurement team. The Organ Procurement Organization coordinators never talk to the family until after brain death has been accepted. The transplant team and patient doctors are two separate entities.
3. Donation will mutilate the body, causing disfigurement.
   Answer: NO, the procurement process is a surgical procedure performed in an operating room. There is one clean cut down the middle of the chest Doctors for each organ come to get the organ needed.
4. Families will be charged for the donation.
   Answer: NO, there is no charge to the donor; the transplant recipient pays for the transplant.
5. If you have another disease, you cannot be a donor.
   Answer: NO, yes you can. Each organ is tested separately.
6. The rich and famous are moved to the top of the list.
   Answer: NO, you cannot buy organs and people are moved up the list based on his or her need.
7. I am too old.
   Answer: NO, from babies to senior citizens can donate.
8. It is against my religion.

Answer: NO, most religions support organ, tissue, and eye donation.

How can I become an organ donor?
1. Register on your state registry. Texas Registry is: http://www.donatelifetexas.org
2. Talk to your family: tell your family what you want!
3. Sign a donor card.
4. Designate a decision on your driver's license.
5. Living donation: You can designate the organ.

2. CMO

CMO: *COMFORT MEASURES ONLY*

This is usually used by hospice and solves the fear of being in pain. The patient is not on any life support and is given only medications (not injections) for comfort purposes. Examples: morphine patch, morphine tablets, or a drying patch for the moisture that happens in the dying process. This is a choice that can be written in a Physician Directive.

3. DNR/AND

DNR: *DO NOT RESUSCITATE*
AND: *ALLOW NATURAL DEATH*

DNR is a medical order that must be issued by the physician stating that special treatments are not to be used in the case of end of life. This involves CPR (cardiopulmonary resuscitation), a procedure performed when the heart and lungs stop working (*cardio* means "heart"/ *pulmonary* means "lung").
DNR needs to be documented.
This choice can be for the hospital or in the home.
If a patient is being transported in an emergency vehicle from hospital to their home or facility, an "Out-of-Hospital DNR/AND" will be required.
If using hospice care, one of their team members can help obtain the needed form.
If a patient has a Living Will, do you need a DNR, too? Yes.
A Living Will is written in advance and outlines what medical treatment is wanted or not wanted. This is a choice that can be written in a Physician Directive.

4. Hydration

This is an artificial form of treatment that uses intravenous (IV) feeding of fluids like water or glucose. This is a choice that can be written in a Physician Directive.

5. Life support

This is an artificial form of treatment that involves intubation with a ventilator or respirator (tube in nose or mouth), catheterization, and monitors for the heart rate, blood pressure, and vital organs. This is a choice that can be written in a Physician Directive.

6. Nutrition

This is an artificial form of treatment that involves a feeding tube that goes in the nose down to the stomach or the feeding tube goes directly into the stomach. When a person gets close to death, that person does not have an appetite. The digestive system shuts down. This is a choice that can be written in a Physician Directive.

<u>What about making these decisions?</u>
1. Who decides: If competent, the patient.
    No one can force treatment.
    If patient is unable to make the decisions, must use legal documents.
    (These are discussed in Chapter VIII.)
2. What happens if the patient is declared incompetent and has no advance directives?
    a. Any comments the patient has made to family or relatives will stand as wishes.
    b. The problem: This consumes valuable time and emotional energy.
        Comfort measures are delayed; have to wait too long to get started.
3. How does one make such decisions?
    a. Anticipate what lies ahead: symptoms – medications – hospice – choices?
    b. Define what it is you are trying to accomplish.
    c. Define what your "help" is.
    "Help" is defined as "assistance," "relief," "remedy."
4. How does one ever refuse or withdraw treatment for a loved one?
    a. Ask yourself, "What does the patient want?"
    b. Get all the information you need.
    c. Confer with family members.
    d. Remember the patient's wishes – do not be swayed!

<u>Summary</u>

With all of the end-of-life choices that are available, it is difficult to know what one really wants. However, whether for ourselves or for our loved ones, there can be a magical opportunity that we will not want to miss! This is a chance that we have to answer the important questions and to be part of the dying process. Making decisions when healthy is so much easier than when actually involved emotionally in an end-of-life situation. One must weigh the pros and cons for each choice. It is a personal decision that no one else can make. Yes, others can have an influence, but the final decision is ours. Once decisions are made, they should be put in writing. This is where legal documents

come in. Legal documents are discussed and examples are included in
the next chapter, Chapter VIII.
Choices – Choices….Decisions – Decisions.
What will it be?

RELECT

Questions to guide your reflection:

*What do you want in a doctor? What qualities do you look for?

*How far are you willing to go?

*How much pain can you accept? When will you say stop? What treatment would you
  agree to….if you were told you have:
>   70% chance of extending life
>   20% chance of extending life
>   2 weeks of life left

*What does comfort mean to you?

*What is your quality of life?

*Would you be willing to be an organ donor? If so, what organs? Who/what influenced
  you?

*What choices have you made?

*Who influenced you on your choices?

*What are you going to include on your legal documents?

*Are you comfortable with your decisions? Why?

*Are you ready?

Quotes to ponder:

"Death is 100%."

"Death is an appointment you will keep."

"Enjoy life now…it has no expiration date."

"Worry is interest paid on trouble before it comes."

"You can give without loving, but you cannot love without giving."

Standing on The Seashore...By: Henry Van Dyke

I am standing upon the seashore.

A ship at my side spreads her white sails to the morning breeze and starts for the blue ocean.

She is an object of beauty and strength.

I stand and watch her until at length she hangs like a speck of white cloud just where the sea and sky come to mingle with each other.

Then someone at my side says.....“There, she is gone!”

“Gone where?”

Gone from my sight....That is all.

She is just as large in mast and hull and spar as she was when she left my side and she is just as able to bear the load of lifting freight to her destined port.

Her diminished size is in me, not in her.

And just at the moment when someone at my side says......“There, she is gone!”

There are other eyes watching her coming, and other voices ready to take up the glad shout...

“Here she comes!”

And that is dying.

REACT

Activity   *Have a Heart*

Instructions: Preparation: Provide ground rules and background information on handout.

Class Formation: Sit the class or group in small circles of four to six.

1. Review: Pertinent information on organ donation

2. Tell the story:

Each of you is a cardiac patient with carodiomyopathy, a diseased heart muscle tissue. It is not curable except by transplanting a donor heart. Without this operation, you are not expected to live more than a few months and will be very disabled as time goes by. While there are several significant matching considerations for being a candidate for transplantation, you have all been brought together because you have identical characteristics for a donor organ that is becoming available in the next 24 hours. There is no other equitable procedure for determining which one of you becomes the "chosen" recipient. The group must decide.

You must select the recipient –the fortunate one!

That is your task.

From *Thanatopics: Activities and Exercises for Confronting Death* by J. Eugene Knott, Mary C. Ribar, Betty M. Duson, Marc R. King. Copyright © 1991 by J. Eugene Knott, Mary C. Ribar, Betty M. Duson, Marc R. King. Reprinted by permission of the author.

3. **Review Ground Rules.**
   a. Time: 30 minutes
   b. You cannot opt out; no self-sacrifices are allowed.
   c. You are to argue for your selection by building a case for yourself based on your actual life circumstances and history.
   d. You may *argue for or against* the inclusion of others.
   e. Decide who will receive the transplant.
4. **Provide the following background information.**
   a. Prior to illness, successful transplant recipients in the past were more likely to be married, employed, near ideal weight, successful in coping with a life crisis, flexible, optimistic, religious, and involved in a gratifying hobby.
   b. Previous heart transplant recipients have experienced some complications following surgeries including depression, immune system suppression leading to possible life-threatening infections, and possible rejection of the donor heart.
   c. Survival rate ranges from:
   1 day to over 20 years.
   Most have lived fewer than five years.
   But survival experience is lengthening.
5. **Time: 30 minutes**
   You will have 30 minutes for deliberation.
   You will have a 5-minute warning before time is up.
6. **You may begin.**
7. **Stop – Time is up.**
8. **Reflection:**
   a. What critical factors influenced choice:
   medical –psychological – family – any other?
   b. Any solutions proposed? How were they dealt with?
   c. What behaviors were evident in arguing? in the decision?
   d. What values were factors in the selection? Why?
   e. How often was dying, consequences, or death mentioned?
   f. During the selection process, was there a motivation to make the decision by another method such as coin toss or drawing straws? Did this method work? Why?
   g. To what extent did the group try an objective route: using a formula, point system, or rating in a hierarchy manner? Was this method effective? Why?
   h. How did participating in this "real decision" impact you?
   i. What reactions and insights have you gained?
   j. How were your personal values, goals, and interpersonal skills involved? Were they critical? Were you focused?

Activity   *Making the List?*

Instructions: 1. List four choices you would make in end of life.
2. For each choice, state why you chose what you did.
3. Who would you tell?

Activity   *Imagination – The Invitation*

Instructions: Read the actions and then ask the following questions:
Time: Leave 20–40 seconds between each action or thought
1. Place your head on your desk and close your eyes.
2. You have just received bad news – a rapid cancer.
3. You only have one week to live.
4. The invitation is here – let it come in.
5. You are letting your mind go through the process.
6. Oh, things are happening so fast…
7. Where are you?
8. Who is there?
9. Oh my…here come the choices: DNR-Life Support–Feeding Tube?
10. The doctors – what are they doing?
    a. Does your doctor know your wishes?
    b. Does he or she know what you want?
    c. Does he or she know what you do not want?
11. The decisions?
    a. Are my decisions made?
    b. Does my spouse, family know what they are?
    c. Where are the documents?
12. Am I comfortable?
13. Am I ready?
14. Yes, I have accepted the invitation!

Follow-up:
1. What happened when you heard the news?
2. Where were you?
3. Were your wishes known? Were your wishes carried out?
5. Were you comfortable?
6. Were you ready? How did you let the invitation come in?

Option: Can repeat the above:
1. You are at the bedside of your spouse.
2. You are with your best friend.

RECOMMENDED TERMS/ IMPORTANT PEOPLE/WEBSITES

Terms

Brain Dead: Brain is out of order and does not function.

Clinical Death: Absence of pulse, respiration, and/or blood pressure; cold with a mottled color.

CMO: Comfort measures only.

Cold Water Caloric: Test used to determine brain dead: water in the ear to see if there is eye movement.

Coma: A very deep sleep; seems like heavy anesthesia; a prolonged state of deep unconsciousness.

DNR: Do not resuscitate.

Fredericks Spot: A small red spot on one side of the lower back (hip) that is in the shape of a butterfly symbolizing the death process has begun.

Hydration: Use of an IV to provide the body fluids.

Persistent Vegetative
State: A twilight zone between life and death.

Quality of life: The balance of life and quality together; a yardstick that measures the outcome of one's healthcare and the resources that provide better health for an individual; the "adjusted life years" that help us live longer.

Rigor mortis: Stiffness of the body following death.

Important people

Dr. Atul Gawande, MD, MPH: American surgeon, author, and public health researcher; General and Endocrine surgeon at Brigham and Women's Hospital; Professor in the Department of Health Policy and Management at Harvard School of Public Health; Professor in the Department of Surgery at Harvard Medical School; Executive Director of Ariadne labs

Ezra Klein: Editor in Chief for Vox Media, columnist for The Washington Post, known as "American Blogger"

Leigh Kackley: Organ recipient of a liver

Dr. Ronald Wilson, MD. Central Texas Nephrology, Waco, Texas

Websites

Gina Comparini. "Donors Wanted: Navigating the path to organ and tissue donation," 2003.

http://journalism.berkeley.edu/projects/transplants/opo.html

http://txorgansharing.org

MSN.com: Vox Topics

Organ Procurement Organization: http://journalism.berkeley.edu/projects/transplants/opo.html

Texas Organ Registry: www.DonateLife.Texas.org

United Network for Organ Sharing: www.unos.org

NOTES

VIII

Legal Issues in Death…

"Are there really documents for dying?"

READ

In examining the reality of death, it is possible to recognize that there is such a thing as a good death. Upon this realization, there are questions that may begin to rise:

Am I ready?
Am I prepared?
Do I have choices?
How can I be assured that my wishes will be carried out?

In the past, nature used to make the call, and people knew how to respond. In today's world, medicine has given us the choice of when and how we will die. Because 80 percent of deaths usually take place in a professional environment, like a hospital or nursing home, we have lost our familiarity with death. Approximately forty percent of people spend more than ten days in intensive care under bright lights, connected to technology, and away from family. There is even the possibility of seeing hospital specialists instead of one's own family physician. We can prepare ourselves for these possibilities by educating ourselves about the choices that will determine the kind of death that we have.

It is easy to ignore documents like Living Wills and Advance Directives. To pay attention to them means admitting the reality of our eventual death. As uncomfortable as it is to pay attention to these documents, it also means to have the kind of death we want. The old saying, "Don't put off until tomorrow what you can do today" applies to these decisions. Additionally, by making our own choices for the care we want, the burden will not settle on our families.

Questions to consider:
1. Can we choose how we want to die?
2. What are our choices?
3. What are the documents in which we can state our choices?

Steps To Take
1. Communicate: Say or write what you want.
2. Complete Advance Directives
    a. Durable Power of Attorney
    b. Medical Power of Attorney – Health Care Proxy
    b. Directive to Physician and Family or Surrogates: Living Will
    c. Out-of-Hospital Do-Not-Resuscitate Order
3. Make a Will or Trust.
4. Other document possibilities
5. Have knowledge about the Health Insurance Portability and Accountability Act.

1. Communicate

Communication sounds easy, but how do you talk to someone about your wishes for your own death, or about their wishes for their death? Bringing up the taboo topic at dinner is probably not the thing to do, but we can set a time for the conversation. Here are some ways to help set up the "death" conversation for you or for a loved one:

- Imagine a real situation.
- Talk about a "setback" of the illness or the illness of a friend.
- Include the physician or pastor in the conversation.
- Schedule a time and place where you will not be interrupted or hurried.
- Listen (Chapter VI).
- Ask the person, "Why do you say or want that?"
- Repeat back to him or her what was said.
- Make a list of key points.
- Hug and cry – that's ok.

2. Complete Advance Directives

What are they? Why do you need them? What documents are needed?

Defining Advance Directives

Advance Directives are documents that state your choices about medical treatment or name someone to make decisions about your medical treatment if you are unable to make these decisions for yourself.

They are called Advance Directives because they are signed in advance to let your doctor and other healthcare providers know your wishes concerning medical treatment. Through Advance Directives, you can make valid decisions about your future medical care. The directives protect you and your family from potential suffering and excessive expenses in care at the end of life.

Why do you need Advance Directives?

1. Because you have the legal right to make choices about your own health care.
   Treatment decisions are personal and are usually based on one's values. If you become seriously ill or experience a serious accident, you may not be able to communicate your wishes, or your family may not agree on what is best for you. There may be a time when the courts will step in and appoint a guardian to make those decisions for you.

2. Because accidents and terminal illness can happen to anyone at any age.
   Advance directives are for everyone—not just the chronically ill or the elderly.

3. Because this allows the opportunity for you to remove the burden of decision-making from your family or court.
   When you are incompetent or cannot communicate what you want due to sickness or injury, someone has to make those decisions for you. Family members often have different opinions on what is best for you, and these simple documents can help avoid guardianship and lessen conflict in the family.

4. Because this provides healthcare providers with guidance on how to care for you.

5. Because this allows you to choose the person in charge of your care *before* you have a serious accident or illness.

6. Because this provides a statement from you to direct emergency medical services and hospital emergency room personnel to withhold cardiopulmonary resuscitation or other life-sustaining measures, if you do not want them.

<u>What Advance Directives are needed?</u>
(Document samples are the at end of this chapter.)
The documents are for the "dying person" (*still alive*) and their family.

Durable Power of Attorney

> *A legal document that designates a person (s) to act on your behalf regarding your <u>affairs</u> immediately or in the event of your incapacity. (Document can be obtained from an attorney)*

pg. 107

Medical Power of Attorney

> *A legal document that allows you to appoint another person (as your agent) <u>to make medical decisions</u> for you if you should become temporarily or permanently unable to make those decisions yourself.*

pg. 111

Directive to Physician and Family and Surrogates: (Living Will)

> *A legal document that instructs your doctor or other healthcare professionals whether you want life-sustaining treatments or procedures administered to you if you are in a terminal condition or in an irreversible condition. Need to state what you want and what you do not want. It is called a "Living Will" because it takes effect while you are still living.*

pg. 117

Out-of-Hospital Do-Not-Resuscitate Order

> *Directs healthcare professionals (emergency medical services. hospital emergency room personnel, other healthcare professionals) acting in an out-of-hospital setting to withhold cardiopulmonary resuscitation and other life sustaining treatment.*
>
> *Applies to cardiopulmonary resuscitation, advanced airway management, artificial ventilation, defibrillation, transcutaneous cardiac pacing.*
>
> *(Document can be obtained through hospice or state Department of Health Services)*

pg. 107

<u>Common questions and answers concerning Advance Directives</u>
Do I have to have an Advance Directive?

No.   It is entirely up to you whether you want to prepare any documents. But if questions arise about the kind of medical treatment that you want or do not want, Advance Directives may help to solve these important issues.

if you are competent you make the decision

What if I do not have a Directive to Physician?

If you do not have a Directive to Physician, Medical Power of Attorney, or guardian, you will receive medical care. There is a greater chance that you will receive more treatment or more procedures than you may want. Your doctor will base the decision of life-sustaining treatment on your wishes, if he or she knows what your wishes are. If your wishes are unknown, your doctor and at least one other person will decide. Under Texas state law, the person included will be in order of priority:

1. Your guardian – if the court has appointed one to make health-care decisions
2. Your spouse
3. Your adult children – one who is reasonably available for consultation
4. Your parents
5. Your nearest living relative
6. Your doctor, with agreement of another doctor who is not in-volved in your care

• Note: If there is a conflict, the court will make the decision.

How do I decide on an agent?

The person should be someone you *know* and *trust* and is at least 18 years old. When selecting a healthcare agent, ask yourself if that person:

Will be willing to speak on your behalf?
Will be willing to act on your wishes?
Lives close by or can travel if necessary?
Knows you well?
Will be able to handle the responsibility?
Will talk to you about sensitive issues?
Will listen to your wishes?
Will be available if necessary?
Will handle conflicting opinions?
Will be a strong advocate for you?

Can I have more than one agent?

Yes.   More than one agent is not required, but you may designate alternates who may also act for you, if your primary agent is unavailable, unable, or unwilling to act. Alternate agents have the same decision-making powers as the primary agent.

How will I know my treatment choices?

Your doctor must inform you about your medical condition and what the different treatments can do for you. Once you understand the treatments that are available, you make the choice, not the doctor. The decision is yours.

What is informed consent?

Informed consent means that you are able to understand the nature, extent, and probable consequences of the proposed medical treatments. You are able to make rational evaluations of risks and benefits of those treatments as compared with the risks and benefits of alternate procedures, and you are able to communicate that understanding.

Who do I talk to about the Advance Directives?

Talk to the people closest to you and who are concerned about your care. Discuss directives with your doctor, family, friends, and other people such as a lawyer or clergy.

When do the directives become effective?

Your agent's authority begins:
1. When your doctor certifies that you lack the competence to make healthcare decisions and you cannot speak for yourself.
2. When your doctor has diagnosed and certified in writing in your medical records that you have a terminal or irreversible condition.

How do I know if my directives will be followed?

Directives are usually followed, if they comply with the law. Federal law requires your healthcare providers to give you their written policies concerning advance directives. If a doctor or healthcare provider cannot or will not follow your directives due to moral, religious, or professional reasons, he or she must tell you immediately. Then he or she must help you transfer to another doctor or facility that will do what you want.

What do I need for my Advance Directives to be valid?

1. The directive does not have to be notarized.
2. You do not have to use a lawyer, but they can be helpful in your discussion.
3. You must:
   a. Sign your documents in front of witnesses.
   b. Sign in front of two witnesses:
      1) Witnesses must be 18 years old.
      2) Competent; in good mental health
      3) At least one witness must be **disinterested** *(see below)*.
   c. Who cannot sign as a witness?
      1) Your relative, blood or marriage.
      2) Anyone who is entitled to any part of your estate upon your death.
      3) Anyone you have designated to make treatment decisions for you.
      4) Your attending physician or your physician's employee.
      5) An employee at a healthcare facility where you are a patient.

What do I do with the completed directives?

1. Keep originals in a safe place (not a safe deposit box) where family members can get to them.
2. Give one copy to:
   a. Your doctor and other healthcare providers for your files.
   b. Your spouse and other family members.
   c. Your lawyer.
   d. Your clergy person.
   e. Any local hospital or facility where you may be residing.
   f. Named agents.

What if I change my mind?

Advance Directives can be reversed or revoked at any time regardless of mental competency by:

1. Canceling or destroying the directive.
2. Completing a new directive to replace the old one (s).
3. Signing and dating a written statement revoking the directive.
4. Orally revoking the directive.
5. Telling your healthcare provider that you have changed your mind.

Are there any decisions my agent cannot make?

Yes.   Law (in Texas) prohibits your agent from consenting to:
1. Voluntary inpatient mental health services.
2. Convulsive treatment.
3. Psychosurgery.
4. Abortion.
5. Omitting care intended primarily for your comfort.

Will Advance Directives affect my Will or my insurance?

No.

Other guidelines that will help you with your decisions:

1. Directives are free.
2. They do not involve decisions about your money or property.
3. They only cover medical treatment decisions.
4. They do not restrict procedures, treatments, or medications intended to make you more comfortable or to be used for pain management.

3. Make a Will and Trust

Death is never timely. Death confronts the family with grief and bereavement, presents the need to readjust emotionally, as well as the need to adjust financially; accompanying these is an unknown vision for the future. A Will or Trust is viewed after a death has occurred. Additionally, a death certificate must be issued and the estate of the deceased must be passed to others.

What is an Estate?

An estate consists of property, both real and personal, that the decedent owns at the time of death. Real property includes any land as well as improvements to the land, oil, gas, and mineral interests. Personal property is everything else besides the real: cash, bank accounts, clothing, household furnishings, motor vehicles, stocks and bonds, life insurance policies, and government, retirement, or employee benefits. Upon death, title to the decedent's property passes immediately to the beneficiaries under the decedent's will or to the heir-at-law if there is no will. The will must be approved in court or if there is no will, the courts determine who the heirs are. This protects the rights of the family, those entitled to property, and the creditors of the estate.

Defining and making a Will

Will: *A legal document stating how the person's property is to be distributed at death. Distribution of property and possessions, disposing of one's assets, or anything that expresses intent following a death.*

Testator: *A person who leaves a will in force at his or her death.*

Intestate: *Dying without a will.*

Purpose: *Identifies who will receive your property upon your death. Identifies the individual who will serve as your executor. Identifies the individual (s) whom you wish to serve as guardian or alternate guardians of your minor children. Provides how debts and taxes will be allocated among beneficiaries. Identifies the powers and responsibilities of your executor. Provides plan for federal estate taxes. Exercises power of appointment – recipients of property held in trust. Reduces the burden of administering your estate by making your will easier to probate.*

Questions and answers concerning a Will

When do I need a Will?
If you: are married
           have children
           you need to name a guardian for any reason
           work
           have property

How old can you be to sign a Will?
Legal age: 18 or older

A trust upon death.

What does probate mean?
It is the legal process to recognize a Will.

What to know about probate?
- No one inherits debts.
- Creditors get paid first.
- If not enough money, write creditors and say "no money," then there is no reason to probate the Will.

Note:
State laws will vary from state to state.
Texas: Very easy to probate a Will.
California and Florida: takes a long time.

How is a Will written?
There are three kinds of Wills: oral, handwritten, typed

1. Oral Will:	Applies only to personal property. Valid only if made by the decedent in his or her last illness and at home, except when he or she becomes sick away from home and dies before returning home.
2. Handwritten Will:	Known as a *"Holographic Will."* Must be in the testator's handwriting and signed by him or her. It does not need to be witnessed. It can be written on anything. Typewritten words may not be included in a holographic will. "This is my last will and testament" is usually sufficient to show intent.
3. Typewritten Will:	Known as a "Formal Will." A well-drafted typewritten Will is more likely to carry out the decedent's intent. Can be prepared by the lay person or an experienced attorney. Must be signed/dated by testator. May be signed/dated by another person at his or her direction and in his or her presence. Witnesses: Must have two witnesses above the age of 14 and be signed in the presence of the testator.

<u>Defining and making a Trust</u>

Trust: *A Trust is usually created during the lifetime of its grantor and may be revocable or irrevocable. A Testamentary Trust is created under the decedent's Will and becomes irrevocable upon the decedent's death. Most people do not write a Trust.*

Purpose: *Provides for the management and preservation of your estate.*
Provides methods for reducing or eliminating taxes.
Provides for the disposition of your estate in a manner that cannot be accomplished through outright bequests.
Avoids probate in some cases.
Protects assets from your beneficiaries' creditors.

A Trust for your children:
Write a statement that states the age at which you want your children to receive their portion of the trust fund.
Recommended Age: 25 is the normal choice.

4. Other document possibilities

<u>Guidance Letter or Love Letter</u>
This is a written letter of non-binding instructions and guidance to family and friends. One can include:

1. An explanation of why you did what you did.
2. A statement "that you still love them."
3. An explanation of where items and possessions of the estate are located.
4. An explanation of gifts, notes, or other things.

<u>The Gift</u>
Parents or relatives may choose to give a monetary gift to their children or relatives each year to make sure the money is distributed before a death or illness. By law, one may give up to $11,000 per person per year to each child.

5. Knowledge about The Health Insurance Portability and Accountability Act (HIPAA)

<u>What is HIPAA?</u>
Here is a lawyer's response to HIPAA in regards to one's medical information …

"The Health Insurance Portability and Accountability Act of 1996 (HIPAA) is a <u>federal law</u> which significantly limits the parties to whom a physician or insurance company may release a patient's medical information. With very few exceptions, a provider may release a patient's medical information only to the patient or a third party expressly authorized by the patient. In order to ease communication between a patient's medical providers and his family, the patient should consider signing a HIPAA authorization, permitting providers to share medical information with the listed persons. **An authorization may include family members, friends, religious leaders and anyone else whom the patient might want to receive medical information. The HIPAA authorization must be distinguished from a medical power of attorney in that the HIPAA authorization does not permit the named agents to make decisions for the patient; it merely permits them to receive information.** The medical power of attorney is used to authorize an agent to make decisions for a patient in the event the patient is unable to do so for himself."

The three parts of HIPAA

Part 1:   *HIPAA Privacy Rule*

The federal law that provides protection for personal health information held by covered entities (people/ physicians/hospitals/labs involved, etc.) and gives patients the right with respect to that information.
In other words…You have the right over your health information and you set the rules and limits on who can look at and receive your health information whether it is electronic, written, or oral.
This rule is balanced so that it permits the disclosure of personal health information needed for patient care and other important purposes.

Part 2:   *HIPAA Security Rule*

The federal law specifies a series of administrative, physical, and technical safeguards for covered entities to use to assure the confidentiality, integrity, and availability of electronic protected health information.
In other words…the law protects electronic health information and requires entities (people/physicians/hospitals/labs involved, etc) to ensure that electronic health information is secure.

Part 3:   *Confidentiality Provisions of the Patient Safety Rule*

This part of the law protects identifiable information being used to analyze patient safety events and improves patient safety.

<u>Who is covered by the Privacy Act?</u>
The Privacy Act applies to health plans, healthcare clearinghouses, and any healthcare provider who transmits health information in electronic form.

Health insurers and providers who are covered entities (people/physicians/hospitals/labs involved, etc.) must comply with your right to:

1. Ask to see and get a copy of your health records.
2. Have corrections added to your health information.
3. Receive a notice that tells you how your health information may be used and shared.
4. Decide if you want to give your permission before your health information can be used or shared for certain purposes, such as for marketing.
5. Get a report on when and why your health information was shared for certain purposes.
6. Know if you believe your rights are being denied or your health information isn't being protected, that you can:
    a. File a complaint with your provider or health insurer.
    b. File a complaint with the U.S. government.

 <u>Summary</u>

What is the answer to the question, "Are there really documents for dying?" The answer is, "Yes." Remember, any documents related to health care decisions are protected, and you have the right to know to whom you are releasing the documents, and for what purpose they will be used. The time to prepare these important documents is not in the heat of death, but in the healthy and uneventful times when emotions are not flowing so rapidly. Yes, these are difficult decisions, but they are necessary. Making these decisions is not easy for anyone. However, once made, relief and peace often accompanies both the one who has made the decisions, and the one designated to fulfill the wishes of their loved one.

RELECT

Questions to guide your reflection:

Are you prepared?

Who would your "Power of Attorney" be?

Would your "Medical Power of Attorney" be the same as your Power of Attorney? If a different person, who would it be?

What would you want written on your "Directive to Physician"? –What do you want and what do you not want?

How would you answer the "Out-of- Hospital Do Not Resuscitate Order"?

Who would your two witnesses be?

Think about communication to your parent, family member or friend. Where would you sit down to talk about your death choices?

How would you bring up the subject of death to your parents?

List five items you would put in your will, stating where they are and who gets them.

Quotes to ponder:

"Life takes away your values, but it does not take away your responsibilities."

"Life happens to all of us whether we want it to or not."

"Every day is a gift, that is why it is called the present."

REACT

Activity　　　*Guest Speaker About Legal Issues in Death*

Instructions:　Invite a guest speaker to come speak to class:
　　　　　　　Lawyer or paralegal who has probate or elder law experience
　　　　　　　1.　Have students take notes on lecture.
　　　　　　　Next class time:
　　　　　　　1.　Divide class into groups of three to five students.
　　　　　　　2.　Share notes and discussion on guest lecture.
　　　　　　　3.　Review legal documents provided in manual.
　　　　　　　Teacher: Ask for any questions or concerns.

Activity   *Writing a Guidance or Love letter*

Instructions: 1. Provide students with a blank piece of 8 ½ × 11 paper.
                   2. Have students write a "Guidance Letter" to their parents explaining the following:
                       a. A list of gifts and who receive those gifts.
                       b. Where gifts are located.
                       c. Love for the parents, family, and friends.
                   3. Sign and date the letter.
                   4. Provide each student with an envelope.
                   5. Have students place the letter in the envelope, seal, sign across seal, address, date on the outside.

Activity   *Writing Your Will*

Instructions: 1. Provide students with a blank piece of 8 ½ × 11 paper.
                   2. Have students write their will.
                   3. Have students sign and date.
                   4. Provide each student with an envelope.
                   5. Have students place their will in the envelope, seal, sign across seal, write title on front, date on the outside.

RECOMMENDED TERMS/ IMPORTANT PEOPLE/WEBSITES

Terms

Artificial nutrition and hydration:	The provision of nutrients or fluids by a tube inserted in a vein, under the skin in the subcutaneous tissues, or in the stomach (gastrointestinal tract).
Durable:	Effective even after losing capacity; lasting.
HIPAA:	The Health Insurance Portability and Accountability Act of 1996.
Irreversible condition:	A condition, injury, or illness that 1. May be treated, but is never cured or eliminated. 2. Leaves a person unable to care for or make decisions for the person's own self. 3. Without life-sustaining treatment provided in accordance with the prevailing standard of medical care, is fatal.
Life-sustaining treatment:	The treatment that, based on reasonable medical judgment, sustains the life of a patient and without which the patient will die. This includes

medications and artificial life support like mechanical breathing machines, kidney dialysis, artificial hydration and nutrition. The term does not include administration of pain management medication, procedures for comfort care, or any other medical care to alleviate pain.

Terminal condition:	An incurable condition caused by injury, disease, or illness that according to reasonable medical judgment will produce death within six months, even with available life-sustaining treatment provided in accordance with the prevailing standard of medical care.

Important people

Elisa Dillard Rainey, Rainey and Rainey Attorneys at Law, LP. Waco, Texas

Websites and contact information for help

American Bar Association	website: www.abanet.org
Children of Aging Parents	1-800-227-7294 www.caps4cargivers.org
Family Caregivers Alliance	1-800-445-8106 website: www.caps4caregivers.org
Funeral Consumer Alliance	1-800-765-0107 www.funeral.org
Heart of Texas Council of Governments:	1514 South New Road Waco, Texas 76711 254-292-1800
Legal Hotline for Texans:	815 Brazos, Suite 1100 Austin, TX 78701 512-477-3950 1-800-622-2520
Legal Zoom.com	Provides documents and help in completing legal documents.
National Alliance for Caregiving	1-301-718-8444 website: www.caps4caregiving.org
National Family Caregivers Association	1-800-896-3650 website: www.nfcacares.org
If in Texas: Contact: Your local:	Department of Aging & Disability Services Area Agency on Aging

NOTES

STATUTORY DURABLE POWER OF ATTORNEY

Disclaimer: Information not legal advice.
THE POWERS GRANTED BY THIS DOCUMENT ARE BROAD AND SWEEPING. THEY ARE EXPLAINED IN THE DURABLE POWER OF ATTORNEY ACT, CHAPTER XII, TEXAS PROBATE CODE. IF YOU HAVE ANY QUESTIONS ABOUT THESE POWERS, OBTAIN COMPETENT LEGAL ADVICE. LEGAL ADVICE INVOLVES THE APPLICATON OF LEGAL KNOWLEDGE AND SKILLS BY A LICENSED ATTORNEY TO YOUR SPECIFIC CIRCUMSTANCES. THIS DOCUMENT DOES NOT AUTHORIZE ANYONE TO MAKE MEDICAL AND OTHER HEALTHCARE DECISIONS FOR YOU. YOU MAY REVOKE THIS POWER OF ATTORNEY IF YOU LATER WISH TO DO SO.

I,   (*Your Name*)   _____

    (*Address*)   _____

    (*City*)   _____(*State*)_____

appoint

    (*Name of agent*)_____

    (*Address*)   _____

    (*City*)   _____(*State*)_____

to act for me in any lawful way with respect to all of the following powers except for a power that I have crossed out below:

TO WITHHOLD A POWER, YOU MUST CROSS OUT EACH POWER WITHHELD:

> Real property transactions
> Tangible personal property transactions
> Stock and bond transactions
> Commodity and option transactions
> Banking and other financial institution transactions
> Business operation transactions
> Insurance and annuity transactions
> Estate, trust, and other beneficiary transactions
> Claims and litigation
> Personal and family maintenance
> Benefits from social security, Medicare, Medicaid, or other government
>   programs or civil or military service
> Retirement plan transactions
> Tax matters

IF NO POWER LISTED ON THE PRECEDING PAGE IS CROSSED OUT, THIS DOCUMENT SHALL BE CONSTRUED AND INTERPRETED AS A GENERAL POWER OF ATTORNEY AND MY AGENT (Attorney in fact) SHALL HAVE THE POWER AND AUTHORITY TO PERFORM OR UNDERTAKE ANY ACTION I COULD PERFORM OR UNDERTAKE IF I WERE PERSONALLY PERSENT.

Special Instructions:

Special instructions applicable to gifts *(Initial in front of the following sentence to have it apply):*

_____ Special instructions applicable to gifts:
I grant my agent (attorney in fact) the power to apply my property to make gifts, except that the amount of a gift to an individual may not exceed the amount of annual exclusions allowed from the federal gift tax for the calendar year of the gift.

_____ Special instructions:
I grant the following to limit or extend the powers granted to my agent in this power of attorney. *(List any special instructions on the lines below.)*

_____

_____

_____

_____

UNLESS YOU DIRECT OTHERWISE ABOVE, THIS POWER OF ATTORNEY IS EFFECTIVE IMMEDIATELY AND WILL CONTINUE UNTIL IT IS REVOKED.

CHOOSE ONE OF THE FOLLOWING ALTERNATIVES BY CROSSING OUT THE ALTERNATIVE NOT CHOSEN:

A) **This power of attorney is not affected by my subsequent disability or incapacity.**

B) **This power of attorney becomes effective upon my disability or incapacity.**

YOU SHOULD CHOOSE ALTERNATIVE (A) IF THIS POWER OF ATTORNEY IS TO BECOME EFFECTIVE ON THE DATE IT IS EXECUTED.

IF NEITHER (A) NOR (B) IS CROSSED OUT, IT WILL BE ASSUMED THAT YOU CHOSE ALTERNATIVE (A).

If alternative (B) is chosen and a definition of my disability or incapacity is not contained in this power of attorney, I shall be considered disabled or incapacitated for purposes of this power of attorney if a physician certifies in writing at a date late than the date this power of attorney is executed that, based on the physician's medical examination of me, I am mentally incapable of managing my financial affairs. I authorize the physician who examines me for this purpose to disclose my physical or mental condition to another person for purposes of this power of attorney. A third party who accepts this power of attorney is fully protected from any action taken under this power of attorney that is based on the determination made by a physician of my disability or incapacity.

I agree that any third party who receives a copy of this document may act under it. Revocation of the durable power of attorney is not effective as to a third party until the third party receives actual notice of the revocation. I agree to indemnify the third party for any claims that arise against the third party because of reliance on this power of attorney.

If any agent named by me dies, becomes legally disabled, resigns, or refuses to act, I name the following (each to act alone and successively, in the order named) as successor to that agent:

Name of Alternate Agent: _____

Address of Alternate Agent: _____

THE ATTORNEY IN FACT OR AGENT, BY ACCEPTING OR ACTING UNDER THE APPOINTMENT, ASSUMES THE FIDUCIARY AND OTHER LEGAL RESPONSIBILITES OF AN AGENT.

Signed this _____day of _____, 20_____

Your Signature: _____

State of Texas
County of: _____

This document was acknowledged before me on *(Date)* _____/_____/_____
by *(Name of Principle)* _____

Notary Signature: _____

Notary printed name: _____

My commission expires: _____

Notary Seal: _____

Durable Power of Attorney   **Page -3-**

POWER OF ATTORNEY REVOCATION

Reference is made to certain power of attorney granted by:

_____ (*Your name, Grantor*)

to_____ (*Agent's Name*) ,

and dated _____ / _____ / 20 _____ .

This document acknowledges and constitutes notice that the Grantor hereby revokes, rescinds, and terminates said power-of-attorney and all authority, rights and power thereto effective this date.

Signed under seal this _____ day of_____, 20__

_____

(*Your Signature – the Grantor*)

_____

(*Your Printed or Typed Name - the Grantor*)

State of: _____

County of: _____

On _____/_____/_____(*Date*) before me _____(*Grantor's Name*) personally appeared, known to me (or proved to me on the basis of satisfactory evidence) to be the person whose name is subscribed to the within instrument and acknowledged to me that they executed the same in their authorized capacity, and that by their signature on the instrument the person, or the entity upon behalf of which the person acted, executed the instrument, **WITNESS**, my hand and official seal.

Notary Signature: _____

Notary printed name: _____

My commission expires: _____

Notary Seal: _____

DISCLOSURE STATEMENT for MEDICAL POWER OF ATTORNEY
Advance Directives Act (see §166.163, Health and Safety Code)

> ### THIS IS AN IMPORTANT LEGAL DOCUMENT!
> ### BEFORE SIGNING THIS DOCUMENT, YOU SHOULD KNOW THESE IMPORTANT FACTS:

Except to the extent you state otherwise, this document gives the person you name as your agent the authority to make any and all health care decisions for you in accordance with your wishes, including your religious and moral beliefs, when you are no longer capable of making them yourself. Because "health care" means any treatment, service, or procedure to maintain, diagnose, or treat your physical or mental condition, your agent has the power to make a broad range of health care decisions for you. Your agent may consent, refuse to consent, or withdraw consent to medical treatment and may make decisions about withdrawing or withholding life-sustaining treatment. Your agent may not consent to voluntary inpatient mental health services, convulsive treatment, psycho-surgery, or abortion. A physician must comply with your agent's instructions or allow you to be transferred to another physician.

Your agent's authority begins when your doctor certifies that you lack the competence to make health care decisions.

Your agent is obligated to follow your instructions when making decisions on your behalf. Unless you state otherwise, your agent has the same authority to make decisions about your health care as you would have had.

It is important that you discuss this document with your physician or other health care provider before you sign it to make sure that you understand the nature and range of decisions that may be made on our behalf. If you do not have a physician, you should talk with someone else who is knowledgeable about these issues and can answer your questions. You do not need a lawyer's assistance to complete this document, but if there is anything in this document that you do not understand, you should ask a lawyer to explain it to you.

The person you appoint as agent should be someone you know and trust. The person must be 18 years of age or older or a person under 18 years of age who has had the disabilities of minority removed. If you appoint your health or residential care provider (e.g., your physician or an employee of a home health agency, hospital, nursing home, or residential care home, other than an relative), that person has to choose between acting as your agent or as your health or residential care provider; the law does not permit a person to do both at the same time.

You should inform the person you appoint that you want the person to be your health care agent. You should discuss this document with your agent and your physician and give each a signed copy. You should indicate on the document itself the people and institutions who have signed copies. Your agent is not liable for health care decisions made in good faith on your behalf.

Even after you have signed this document, you have the right to make health care decisions for yourself as long as you are able to do so and treatment cannot be given to you or stopped over your objection. You have the right to revoke the authority granted to your agent by informing your agent or your health or residential care provider orally or in writing, or by your execution of a subsequent medical power of attorney. Unless you state otherwise, your appointment of a spouse dissolves on divorce.

This document may not be changed or modified. If you want to make changes in the document, you must make an entirely new one.

You may wish to designate an alternate agent in the event that your agent is unwilling, unable, or ineligible to act as your agent. Any alternate agent you designate has the same authority to make health care decisions for you.

THIS POWER OF ATTORNEY IS NOT VALID UNLESS IT IS SIGNED IN THE PRESENCE OF TWO COMPETENT ADULT WITNESSES.

THE FOLLOWING PERSONS MAY NOT ACT AS ONE OF THE WITNESSES.

1) **the person you have designated as your agent;**

2) **a person related to you by blood or marriage;**

3) **a person entitled to any part of your estate after your death under a will or codicil executed by you or by operation of law;**

4) **your attending physician;**

5) **an employee of your attending physician;**

6) **an employee of a health care facility in which you are a patient if the employee is providing direct patient care to you or is an officer, director, partner, or business office employee of the health care facility or parent organization of the health care facility; or**

7) **a person who at the time this power of attorney is executed, has a claim against any part of your estate after your death.**

MEDICAL POWER OF ATTORNEY
Advance Directives Act (see §166.164, Health and Safety Code)
DESIGNATION OF HEALTH CARE AGENT

I, _____ (insert your name) appoint:

Name: _____Relationship: _____

Address: _____

City: _____State: _____

Phone: _____

as my agent to make any and all health care decisions for me, except to the extent I state otherwise in this document. This medical power of attorney takes effect if I become unable to make my own health care decisions and this fact is certified in writing by my physician.

Limitations On The Decision Making Authority Of My Agent Are As Follows:

_____

_____

_____

Designation of an Alternate Agent:
(You are not required to designate an alternate agent, but you may do so. An alternate agent may make the same health care decisions as the designated agent if the designated agent is unable or unwilling to act as your agent. If the agent designated is your spouse, the designation is automatically revoked by law if your marriage is dissolved.)

If the person designated as my agent is unable or unwilling to make health care decisions for me, I designate the following persons to serve as my agent to make health care decisions for me as authorized by this document, who serve in the following order:

First Alternate Agent

Name: _____Relationship: _____

Address: _____

City: _____State: _____

Phone: _____

Second Alternate Agent

Name: _____ Relationship: _____

Address: _____

City: _____ State: _____

Phone: _____

The original copy of this document is kept at:

_____

_____

The following individuals or institutions have signed copies:

Name:#1:_____ Relationship:_____

Address: _____

City: _____ State: _____

Phone: _____

Name:#2:_____ Relationship:_____

Address: _____

City: _____ State: _____

Phone: _____

Duration

I understand that this power of attorney exists indefinitely from the date I execute this document unless I establish a shorter time or revoke the power of attorney. If I am unable to make health care decisions for myself when this power of attorney expires, the authority I have granted my agent continues to exist until the time I become able to make health care decisions for myself.

(IF APPLICABLE) This power of attorney ends on the following date:

_____

Prior Designations Revoked:.

I revoke any prior medical power of attorney.

Acknowledgement of Disclosure Statement.

I have been provided with a disclosure statement explaining the effect of this document. I have read and understand that information contained in the disclosure statement.

(YOU MUST DATE AND SIGN THIS POWER OF ATTORNEY)

I sign my name to this medial power of attorney on:

_____ day of _____ Month/Year

at: _____
(City and State)

_____
(Signature)

_____
(Print Name)

Statement of First Witness:

I am not the person appointed as agent by this document. I am not related to the principal by blood or marriage. I would not be entitled to any portion of the principal's estate on the principal's death. I am not the attending physician of the principal or any employee of the attending physician. I have no claim against any portion of the principal's estate on the principal's death. Furthermore, if I am an employee of a health care facility in which the principal is a patient, I am not involved in providing direct patient care to the principal and am not an officer, director, partner, or business office employee of the health care facility or of any parent organization of the health care facility.

First Witness:

Witness Signature: _____ Date/Yr.: _____

Print Name: _____

Address: _____

City: _____ State: _____

Second Witness:

Witness Signature: _____ Date/Yr.: _____

Print Name: _____

Address: _____

City: _____ State: _____

DIRECTIVE TO PHYSICIANS AND FAMILY OR SURROGATES
Advance Directives Act (see §166.033, Health and Safety Code)

This is an important legal document known as an Advance Directive. It is designed to help you communicate your wishes about medical treatment at some time in the future when you are unable to make your wishes known because of illness or injury. These wishes are usually based on personal values. In particular, you may want to consider what burdens or hardships of treatment you would be willing to accept for a particular amount of benefit obtained if you were seriously ill.

You are encouraged to discuss your values and wishes with your family or chosen spokesperson, as well as your physician. Your physician, other health care provider, or medical institution may provide you with various resources to assist you in completing your advance planning. Initial the treatment choices that best reflect your personal preferences. Provide a copy of your directive to your physician, usual hospital, and family or spokesperson. Consider a periodic review of this document. By periodic review, you can best assure that the directive reflects your preferences.

In addition to this advance directive, Texas law provides for two other types of directives that can be important during a serous illness. These are the <u>Medical Power of Attorney</u> and the <u>Out-of-Hospital Do-Not-Resuscitate Order</u>. You may wish to discuss these with your physician, family, hospital representative, or other advisers. You may also wish to complete a directive related to the donation of organs and tissues.

DIRECTIVE

I, _____, recognize that the best health care is based upon a partnership of trust and communication with my physician. My physician and I will make health care decisions together as long as I am of sound mind and able to make my wishes known. If there comes a time that I am unable to make medical decisions about myself because of illness or injury, I direct that the following treatment preferences be honored.

If, in the judgment of my physician, I am suffering with a terminal condition from which I am expected to die within six months, even with available life-sustaining treatment provided in accordance with prevailing standards of medical care:

_____ I request that all treatments other than those needed to keep me comfortable be discontinued or withheld and my physician allow me to die as gently as possible;
OR

_____ I request that I be kept alive in this terminal condition using available life-sustaining treatment.

(This section does not apply to Hospice care.)

If, in the judgment of my physician, I am suffering with an irreversible condition so that I cannot care for myself or make decisions for myself and am expected to die without life-sustaining treatment provided in accordance with prevailing standards of care:

_____ I request that all treatments other than those needed to keep me comfortable be discontinued or withheld and my physician allow me to die as gently as possible; **OR**

_____ I request that I be kept alive in this irreversible condition using available life-sustaining treatment..

(This section does not apply to Hospice care.)

Additional requests:

(After discussion with your physician, you may wish to consider listing particular treatments in this space that you do or do not want in specific circumstances, such as artificial nutrition and fluids, intravenous antibiotics, etc. Be sure to state whether you do or do not want the particular treatment.)

_____

_____

_____

_____

After signing this directive, if my representative or I elect hospice care, I understand and agree that only those treatments needed to keep me comfortable would be provided and I would not be given available life-sustaining treatments.

If I do not have a Medical Power of Attorney, and I am unable to make my wishes known, I designate the following person(s) to make treatment decisions with my physician compatible with my personal values:

1. _____

2. _____

(If a Medical Power of Attorney has been executed, then an agent already has been named and you should not list additional names in this document.)

If the above persons are not available, or if I have not designated a spokesperson, I understand that a spokesperson will be chosen for me following standards specified in the laws of Texas. If, in the judgment of my physician, my death is imminent within minutes to hours, even with the use of all available medical treatment provided within the prevailing standard of care, I acknowledge that all treatments may be withheld or removed except those needed to maintain my comfort. I understand that under Texas law this directive has ho effect if I have been diagnosed as pregnant.

This directive will remain in effect until I revoke it. No other person may do so.

Signed: _____ Date: _____

City: _____ County: _____ State: _____

Two witnesses must sign in the spaces below!

Two competent adult witnesses must sign below, acknowledge that signature of the declarant. The witness designated as <u>Witness I</u> may not be a person designated to make a treatment decision for the patient and may not be related to the patient by blood or marriage. This witness may not be entitled to any part of the estate and may not have a claim against the estate of the patient. This witness may not be the attending physician or an employee of the attending physician. If this witness is an employee of a health care facility in which the patient is being cared for, this witness may not be involved in providing direct patient care to the patient. This witness may not be an officer, director, partner, or business office employee of a health care facility in which the patient is being cared for or of any partner organization of the health care facility.

Witness #1: _____

Witness #2: _____

IX

Today's Debates…

"What are we facing?"

JANUARY

Sunday	Monday	Tuesday	Wednesday	Thursday	Friday	Saturday
	1	2	3	4	5	6
7	8	9	10	11	12	13
14	15	16	17	18	19	20
21	22	23	24	25	26	27
28	29	30	31			

READ

With the baby-boomer generation now having stepped into the "senior citizen" category, it is apparent that end-of-life care will continue to emerge as an issue to be addressed socially, ethically, and politically. With physician-assisted suicide and the right-to-die movement being at the top of some ethical and political conversations during the past few years, it will not be surprising if end-of-life care will lead the way in our country's ongoing healthcare debate and legislation. At first glance, these are issues that may appear to be simple and easy to talk about in an intellectual manner or to pigeonhole for a political debate. However, when a family is faced with the death of a loved one, when the issues become personal and family members are looking each other in the eye at the bedside of their dying loved one, it is probable that the decision-making will be more ambiguous and more difficult. The next generations of adults will be confronted with making both personal and public decisions about not only how they live, but how they die.

The content of this conversation corresponds with what is discussed elsewhere in this book regarding legal issues, physician and medical choices, and listening.

History

Current issues are not new. In order to fully appreciate today's debates, it is helpful to know what has occurred in the past. Below is a brief

121

timeline of approximately 80 years showing a small number of influential events and political decisions that have continued to keep these issues not only cutting edge, but vital for human rights.

1938	The Euthanasia Society of America was founded.
1967–1968	The first "living will" was conceived.
1969	Elizabeth Kubler-Ross writes the book, *On Death and Dying,* which opens more open discussion about end-of-life care.
1973	American Hospital Association created the Patient Bill of Rights, which contains informed consent and the right to refuse treatment.
1974	The first American hospice opened in New Haven, Connecticut.
1975	Karen Ann Quinlan, a 21-year-old, went into a persistent vegetative state after ingesting a combination of alcohol and drugs. She was placed on a respirator. Her parents asked for her to be removed from the respirator, but they were refused. They took this to court and were initially refused the same request.
1976	Karen Ann Quinlan's parents were granted their request by the courts that their daughter be removed from the respirator, but she continued to breathe on her own and lived until 1985, when she died.
1983	Nancy Cruzan, 25 years old, was in a car accident and was in a persistent vegetative state. Her parents went to the court system where they requested that her feeding tube be removed. For three years, their request was denied, but was finally granted in 1990. The feeding tube was removed, and she died 12 days later.
1985	Karen Ann Quinlan died.
1990	Nancy Cruzan died. The legal case of Nancy Cruzan was the first right-to-die case heard by the U. S. Supreme Court. It confirmed the legality of such strict standards for the entire country.
Read more:	*Courts and the End of Life - The Case of Nancy Cruzan* www.libraryindex.com/pages/3143/Courts-End-Life-CASE-NANCY-CRUZAN.html#ixzz0otHiAb2g

*Both Karen Ann Quinlan and Nancy Cruzan were important in the right-to-die movement as they were taken from the institutions' decisions to the public for awareness and into the hands of the people who were facing these decisions.

1997   The state of Oregon's Death With Dignity Act takes effect.

1990s   Dr. Jack Kevorkian, an American pathologist, came to be known as "Dr. Death" due to the number of assisted suicides of patients with which he was associated. He was incarcerated from 1999–2007 after being convicted of second-degree murder. Dr. Kevorkian died June 3, 2011.

1990–2005   Terri Schiavo, a young woman in Florida, entered into a persistent vegetative state after collapsing from a severe medical condition. She was institutionalized for 15 years, living with the assistance of a feeding tube. The conflict in this case was between her husband wanting her feeding tube removed and her parents saying that they did not want it removed. This case captured the country's headlines as local, state, and federal politicians and court systems were involved. Finally, the doctors did remove her feeding tube, and she died several days following.

2005   Terri Schindler Schiavo died.

While by no means is this a definitive timeline of the history of the complicated right-to-die issues in this country, they are some of the important and highlighted events and people who have both brought and kept this subject alive.

Issues

Euthanasia

Intentionally causing the death of a person with the intent to relieve that person's suffering.

Assisted suicide

Helping a person kill himself or herself. In this act, the patient is in control of the process itself; he or she is being assisted by someone who provides the means, e.g., the medicine.

Physician-assisted suicide

A physician assisting a person to kill himself or herself.

Palliative care

Also known as comfort care: "a comprehensive approach to treating serious illness that focuses on the physical, psychological, spiritual, and existential needs of the patient. Its goal is to achieve the best quality of life available to the patient by relieving suffering and controlling pain and symptoms." www.caringinfo.org. Hospice is a type of palliative care.

Healthcare reform

The most recent national legislation that will hopefully address healthcare needs for all people including children, the elderly, and the uninsured. It still remains to be seen what impact this legislation will have on individual lives, counting end-of-life care, in our country.

REFLECT

Questions to guide your reflection:

*Ponder the above issues:
    What thoughts do they cause to rise in your mind?
    What questions do you have as a result of reading and thinking about these issues?

*Have you had a conversation with an important person in your life regarding these issues that might help you clarify what your wishes are, or who would be the one to know your decisions?

*What informs your thoughts and decisions? Religion and beliefs? Family traditions?

*What current issues in health care and end-of-life care do you think will be discussed in a public format in your lifetime? Should there be legislation regarding these issues? Think of three.

Quotes to ponder:

"Death depends on who we are."

"Death is what happens when we die."

REACT

Activity   *In Your Lifetime?*

Instructions: Divide the class into small groups of four or five.
Select one person in the group to be the note taker.
Select another person to be the spokesperson.
Each group will discuss the following questions and be able to
present the information to the class.
Questions:
1. List 3 "dying topics or issues" that you feel will be up for debate
    today or in your lifetime?
    1.
    2.
    3.
2. List 3 reasons why you listed your topics or issues.
    1.
    2.
    3.
3. List 2 things that provided information or influenced your decisions
    when listing your debatable issues.
    (religion, family, etc.)
    1.
    2.

Activity   *Let's Debate**

Instructions: 1. Using the "READ" section above, choose an event, a person, or an
    issue for debate.
2. Divide the class into two halves.
3. Ask each section to give its support for its statements.
4. After a prearranged length of time, debrief with the class to share
    their experiences with questions like these:
    • Did they change their mind due to hearing others' opinions and
       statements?
    • Which argument was the strongest? Weakest?
    • Who was most persuasive? Why?
    • What argument was missing? Was there something that was not
       addressed that should have been?

    *This activity could be used in two ways:
    1. Following a student presentation on one of these issues, this could
       be used as the class activity that accompanies the presentation.
       (See Chapter IV)
    2. This activity could be used by the instructor during the time
       of the class calendar when these current events and ethical issues
       are addressed.

Activity   *Who's Who*

Instructions: 1. Choose one of these people in the timeline given in the "READ" section above: Karen Ann Quinlan, Nancy Cruzan, or Terri Schiavo
2. After researching, compare and contrast their situations that caused them and their lives and deaths to be significant in the court systems and the right-to-die movement.
3. Write a three- to five-page paper that highlights your research and that answers the question, "Why are they important today?"

Activity   *Current Issues*

Instructions: You will be instructed to find two articles in the September 21, 2009, issue of Newsweek magazine in preparation for class. Follow the instructions below.
1. Locate the September 21, 2009, issue of Newsweek magazine. www.newsweek.com.
2. Read the following articles:
    *   *I Was A Teenage Death Panelist* by Jon Meacham
    *   *The Case For Killing Granny...Rethinking end-of-life care* by Evan Thomas
3. Write a two page paper summarizing these two articles. In this summary, include your opinion and reflection about what these articles say about our society's current conversation about end-of-life care.
4. Be prepared to share these papers in a small group format in class.

RECOMMENDED TERMS/ IMPORTANT PEOPLE/WEBSITES

Websites

Nancy Cruzan and Karen Ann Quinlan:
There are a number of websites that give information about Karen Ann Quinlan and Nancy Cruzan, and the situations that brought national spotlights to their final days. Whether websites or printed materials, readers will find biographical data in addition to resources addressing the legal and political battles.

Terri Schiavo*:
There are a number of websites that give information about Terri Schiavo and the situation surrounding her final days. Some give biographical data while others contend with the political and legal battles; still others purport the story of Terri's life, health, and marriage prior to her institutionalization. A simple search will bring the reader more than he or she can digest.

www.dying.about.com/od/palliativeendoflifecare/p/karen_quinlan.htm

www.libraryindex.com/pages/3143/Courts-End-Life-CASE-NANCY-CRUZAN.html

www.endeavorfreedom.org/LivingWillHistory.htm

www.euthanasia.20m.com

www.euthanasia.com

As stated above in regard to Terri Schiavo, there are a number of websites, books, and articles written about Terri Schiavo, Nancy Cruzan, and Karen Ann Quinlan. Because these issues involve politics, ethics, and morals, there is a variety of opinions and points of view written about their lives and their families. It is important to acknowledge this variety and not simply highlight one part of these issues.

NOTES

X

Children and Death...
"This Can't Be!"

READ

Remarkable: *This is just one word that characterizes children who are dying.*

Unique: *This is just one word to describe how children grieve.*

Wrenching: *This is just one word that possibly begins to touch the experience of parents whose child has died.*

Forever: *This is just one word that describes how long the grief of a parent lasts.*

Words are inadequate for all who are touched by the death of a child. But we try. We attempt to put words to this experience because, as intelligent and rational human beings, we strive to wrap our minds around things we do not understand. In every stage of our human development, our lives are spent in trying to make sense of our experience of the world. As adults, we expect to outlive our children. It is the child's death that truly makes no sense. Why did this happen? This question is never answered.

Dying children

As difficult as it is to think about, children die. From newborn to teenager, it is a fact of life. Endurance, courage, resilience, sense of humor, compassion, intuition, and wisdom—all children possess these remarkable qualities, but for those who are dying, these qualities give them a depth and a quality of life that is remarkable. They seem to possess a peace and an almost mystical character that leave the rest of us scratching our heads. The experience of being in the presence of children who are dying is one that is not soon forgotten.

Holding their lives lightly, unlike adults, children have little "emotional baggage" to weigh them down. By the time most people reach adulthood, they have become skilled at living as if their identity is composed of what they do. Our culture teaches that people live their lives based on their roles in family and society. When those roles become diminished, as at the time of death, the question becomes, "Who am I? if I cannot cook dinner for my family anymore? if I cannot drive to the office to work? if I cannot talk anymore?"

Consequently, as adults approach the end of their lives, they may question their worth and the meaning of their lives when they are unable to perform the duties and responsibilities that once gave them identity and purpose. Letting go of doing in order to simply be is difficult emotional and spiritual work.

Children, however, have not lived long enough to carry the burden of proving their worth through performing. They simply live. Living with innocence, enjoying honest relationships, being present to the moment, and speaking truthful words; children have a way of looking life squarely in the eye with no regrets and nothing left unsaid. And so, when they must face their own death, they do so with extraordinary courage.

<u>Characteristics of the dying child?</u>
- 95% of the time, children know they are dying.
- Children use symbolic language.
- Children need family.
- Children want normalcy.
- Children want to be remembered.
- Children need symptom management.

<u>What can we offer to children who are dying?</u>
We can offer . . .
- Care for their physical needs, especially their pain.
- Treatment as living human beings.
- Education about the process of grief.
- Assurance that they will not be left alone.
- Simple, honest, and direct answers to their questions.
- Honest conversation about their illness and disease process.
- To listen to what they want to say.
- A sense of humor, taking their cues.
- A promise that they will not be forgotten.
- To honor their feelings and thoughts.
- Music to help them feel calm, peaceful, happy.
- Normal daily routines.

- To record their voice in a message to their family and friends.
- To write letters or draw pictures to leave for their family and friends.

How do children grieve?

Children grieve uniquely. We need to remember to also pay attention to the siblings who are not ill. Because parents may spend most of their time at doctors' appointments or at the hospital with the child who is ill, siblings who are left behind may be kept by relatives or friends. To prevent confusion in the grieving process, it is important to be honest with both the dying children and the ones who are grieving. Children grieve uniquely as children, not as little adults. Children are active, and they should continue to be active, especially when they are grieving. Children are outwardly focused in their grief as exhibited in their playing one minute and crying the next. They may not be able to sit still in school. Both their anger and sadness may show up in their tears, laughter, and screams. Just because they want to eat the donuts that are at the funeral home when they go to see grandpa who has died, does not mean that they are not grieving. Children like donuts. Let them eat donuts. They may not be able to put words to their feelings, but they are able to put actions to their feelings. They may be able to color and draw their feelings. The depth of their pain is as profound as an adult's pain. Their curiosity and confusion is real and should not be diminished or dismissed. Their tears and cries should not be "shushed." They have a voice and that voice is to be recognized and embraced in times of grief.

How do children respond to death?

Children know when there is something different in their lives. They see and hear. If there is no explanation of what is happening, their imagination takes over and can make the situation worse. The feeling of being alone can leave the message that "we are not going to talk about that." The development and maturity of each individual child does affect his or her reaction and response to death. Let's look at each age group's responses to death.

AGE	RESPONSE TO DEATH
Birth to 1 year of age (*Young infant*)	Up to 6 months of age: 1. No response due to the lack of development of memory capacity for personal relationships. 2. No ability to understand the concept of death. 6 months to 1 year: 1. A loss or separation may be felt. 2. There may be a feeling of vague absence or of something being different.

AGE	RESPONSE TO DEATH
1 to 2 years of age *(Older Infant)*	1. They do not have the ability to put a meaning to death. 2. If the death is of the caregiver or a person they are close to, displeasure or depression is experienced. 3. They can feel the tension and emotional grief experienced in their parents and family. 4. Crying may occur. 5. They may search for the missing person in a way similar to that of a mother cat missing her kitten. 6. There may be a change in sleeping or eating habits.
2 to 4 years of age *(Preschool Age)*	Age 2: 1. Can become aware of death at this early age. 2. May understand by using a visual – dead squirrel, leaves on a tree, or flowers that die, etc. Age 3–4: 1. May feel they caused the death. 2. May show concern for needs of the dead person. 3. Believe death is a punishment. 4. See death as reversible – dead is being still and being alive is moving……seen is movies, cartoons. Etc. 5. Crying may or may not occur. 6. May be clingy – do not want you to get out of their sight – fear in separation. 7. May regress back to younger behaviors – nightmares, thumb sucking, etc. 8. May talk or act as if the person is still alive.
5–9 years of age *(Elementary School Age)*	Age 5: 1. Understand that people die. 2. May think it is temporary – question the use of "never or ever." Age 6–9: 1. Begin to realize death is irreversible; finality of death. 2. Believe it cannot happen to them or their family. 3. May think someone comes to take the person away. 4. Behavior problems may appear possibly in school, having trouble paying attention, fighting, angry. 5. May experience eating or sleeping problems.
9–12 years of age *(Middle School Age)*	1. Knows death is final and is a natural process. 2. May feel threatened with death. 3. May feel guilty; that they caused the death. 4. Understands that death can come at any time. 5. May feel more independent. 6. Physical signs: headaches or stomachaches. 7. Can express their feelings verbally. 8. May get involved in self-destructing behaviors; drugs. 9. May experience depression, sadness, anger, mood swings; lack of interest in things that were formerly of interest to him or her. 10. May see a drop in grades at school.

AGE	RESPONSE TO DEATH
Teen Years _(High School Age)_	1. Know death is final and is a natural process. 2. Realize they can die, but may be in denial: "It can't happen to me." 3. May act like they do not care.
	4. Understand that death can come at any time. 5. May feel guilty; that they caused the death. 6. May participate in reckless, dangerous, or self-destructing behaviors–driving, drinking, drugs etc. 7. The loss can be unbearable. 8. May feel more independent. 9. Physical signs: headaches or stomachaches. 10. May experience depression, sadness, anger, mood swings. 11. May see a drop in grades at school. 12. May see a lack of attention or interest in things that were formerly an interest to him or her.

How do we tell a child that someone has died?

- The information needs to come from someone who has a close relationship with them.
- Pick a location that is quiet and peaceful, a place where you cannot be interrupted.
- Only state the facts that are definite.
- Be concrete, not misleading in language.
- Make sure phrases are understood.
- Allow questions to be asked.
- Be truthful and honest in all statements and replies.
- Simplicity is best.

What can we offer to children who are grieving the loss of a sibling, parent, relative or friend?

- Try to keep your daily routine as normal as possible – keep tasks simple.
- Involve them in the funeral or memorial service rituals and family activities.
- Do not use euphemisms, e.g., "Grandpa is sleeping" or "Mom has gone away."
- Touch—a reminder that they are not alone.
- Warmth—children may feel cold when they are in shock or feel upset.
- Educate them before the funeral:
     "Here is what you will see and hear…"
     "You may touch Grandma, and her body will feel cold."
     "Grandma does not hurt and you will not hurt her if you touch her."
     "It's ok to see adults crying…they feel sad, too."
- Help them to say goodbye by asking them to write a letter or draw a picture that they can put in the casket.

- Ask them what questions they have.
- Be ready to answer their questions as often as they ask them… even the same questions more than once.
- Use honest, simple, direct language.
- Listen with intent, sit or get down on their level, ask them to explain their feelings.
- Reassure children that they are not to blame.
- Encourage them to let you know when they are feeling sad.
- See that they have rest, exercise, and healthy nutrition.
- Remember that children's play and "acting out" is part of their mourning.
- Give them opportunities to release their feelings by drawing pictures, e.g., art therapy. Middle and high school age children may release their feelings through sports as well as art.
- Allow middle school and high school-aged children to make decisions.
- Music that they enjoy.

How do parents grieve?

For the parents of children who are dying or who have died, there are few words to say. Know that their hearts are breaking and that they are going through the one thing that is every parent's greatest fear. Wrenching. Nightmare. Unbelievable. Shock. Unspeakable. There are no words that adequately express this most dreaded experience. Alone is what they feel. Fear of forgetting is what they feel. Unreal is what they feel. Pain is what they feel. Fog is the word that many use to describe their never-ending days upon days during the dying process. Afterwards, when the real work of grief begins, they may feel like they, themselves, are the ones who have died. They might say, "No one knows how we feel."

*The best grief work is done way before a death occurs

For those of us on this side of a parent's grief and pain, one of the greatest gifts we can offer is our presence. While it may not seem like much, to them it means a great deal. More than likely, little can be said that parents will remember during such a profound and traumatic experience. However, they will remember you showing up at the door with a pot of soup and hot bread that says, "I thought you could use some food tonight." We may not know what else to do. It's the symbolism behind the showing up that matters. It will matter for as long as they grieve. Forever.

What can we offer to parents of dying children?

- Assurance that their child's physical needs, including their pain, will be cared for.
- Help with daily tasks, e.g., housecleaning, shopping, meals.
- Financial help, if needed.
- Help with the siblings who are well, e.g., babysit, drive to athletic practices, run errands for school.

- A listening ear.
- Honest answers to their questions.
- Rest, exercise, and good nutrition.
- Good medical care.
- Opportunity for conversation about what they wish to talk about.
- Assurance that they will not be alone.
- Assurance that their child will not be alone.
- Assurance that they will not forget their child.
- Honor, not judgment, for their feelings and thoughts.

What can we offer to parents who are grieving?
- Reminders that their grief will never leave.
- Reminders that their child will not be forgotten.
- Someone to listen to the depth of their pain, guilt, blame, and anger.
- Opportunities to listen to their story, for as many times as they want to tell it.
- Opportunities to listen to their questions.
- Acceptance and honor for their feelings and thoughts.
- Reminders to get rest, exercise, and good nutrition.
- Suggestions for good medical care.
- Care for the other children.
- A reminder that life continues.
- Understanding for their times of silence.
- Opportunities to memorialize their child, e.g., plant a tree, light a candle at a church service, make a quilt.
- Compassion.
- Encouragement to be compassionate and patient with themselves.
- Education about the grief process.
- Companionship and reminders that they are not alone.
- Reminder that they are not going crazy…they are grieving.
- Offer to listen to stories about their child,
  e.g.,"Tell me about the day Josh was born."
    "What were Josh's favorite cookies?"
- To ask to see photos of their child.
- Honor for their feelings and thoughts.
- To bless their tears.
- To make a donation to an organization or cause that is meaningful to the family.
- To remember their child's birthday and contact them on this date.
- To remember their child's date of death and contact them on this date.
- To accompany them to the cemetery.
- Online blogs—some parents find this a helpful avenue in which to share their thoughts and feelings.

• Grief support groups—local hospices are good resources for these.
• A reminder that mothers and fathers grieve differently.
• To contact parents during holidays.
• To remember their children on an ordinary day.

"This can't be…" A parent's grief is forever!

REFLECT

Questions to guide your reflection:

Have you had any experiences with the death of a child? Either when you were a child or more recently? Was this a personal relationship or a professional relationship?

If this was a personal relationship, reflect on your experience by writing what your thoughts and feelings were during that time. If you were a child, what did adults say to you? What was helpful or unhelpful?

If this was a professional relationship, what did you notice about yourself—your own feelings and thoughts?

As you have read this chapter, what has come to your mind about children and death?

Quotes to ponder:

"Grief for a child lasts forever!"

"The most difficult thing in life is saying "Good-bye" and we never get good at it."

"It is not what you leave for them, bu what you leave in them."

"Memories never die."

FAMILY: "Father and Mother, I love you."

REACT

Activity   *Add to the List*

Instructions: Look at each of the five lists in the "Read" section of this chapter.
                    What would you add?
                    Add two items (minimum) to each list.

Activity   *Answering Children's Questions about Death**

Instructions: 1.   <u>State the primary goals of this activity.</u>
To give participants practice in responding to typical queries children address to adults and older siblings about death and dying; to gain some understanding for the developmental complexity of various ways of responding to different levels of understanding; to get feedback on the appropriateness and comfort with which one responds to children's questions.

2.   <u>Setting.</u>
A room large enough for a single seat to be in the middle of a circle of seats adequate for the number of participants. It is recommended that there be a maximum of 8 people per group.

3.   <u>Materials needed.</u>
A set of 3 × 5 cards with the following ages and questions on them in equal numbers to the total of the group. Examples:
- 5-year-old: "Where is dead?"
- 6-year-old: "Will I die when I am old, too?"
- 7-year-old: "Will I see Grandpa again?" (after burial)
- 7-year-old: "Don't people die when they go to the hospital?"
- 4-year-old: "It's only 'bad guys' who get killed. Right?"
- 13-year-old: "I'll never get over her death, will you? (speaking of a peer's death)
- 8-year-old: "Was Mommy angry with me? She didn't say goodbye when she died."
- 9-year-old: "What happens when a person is burned up?" (cremated)
- 6-year-old: "Can you tell me what happens when person dies? Do they go to heaven or hell?"
- 15-year-old: "Why didn't Dad want to go on living?"

4.   <u>Time Needed.</u>
5 minutes per group member plus 20 minutes to debrief

5.   <u>Procedure.</u>
- The group is gathered in a circle with a chair in the center in which each "child" will sit at their turn.
- Each participant is given a card that has the question he or she is to ask and note briefly the age of the questioner.
- Randomly, each group member selects one of the outer circle members to be the respondent (not more than once).

*From *Thanatopics: Activities and Exercises for Confronting Death* by J. Eugene Knott, Mary C. Ribar, Betty M. Duson, Marc R. King. Copyright © 1991 by J. Eugene Knott, Mary C. Ribar, Betty M. Duson, Marc R. King. Reprinted by permission of the author.

- The question and role-play exchange should not exceed 3 minutes each, with the respondent becoming the next role player.
- At the end of the question-and-answer segment, the remainder of the group is asked to critique on the respondent's answer regarding appropriateness (developmentally) and comfort (exhibited while responding, both verbal and nonverbal).

6. Debriefing
   - How did the experience of being asked these questions by a "young person" strike you?
   - Which role was easier? Why?
   - Did you draw on any of your past experiences?
   - Did your anxiety level decrease or increase throughout the exercise? At what points?
   - What developmental differences did you notice?
   - How did questions change depending on developmental level?
   - Was your role as answerer affected by your role as questioner?
   - What other questions would you think appropriate?
   - Are these also questions that might be asked by adults?
   - Was this exercise helpful to you? Why or why not?

Activity   *Children's Books about Death, Dying, and Grief*

Instructions:
1. Divide the class into small groups of four to six.
2. Ask each group to choose a children's book from a collection of books that are in the room. See list of children's books in "Reference" section below.
3. Ask the group to choose someone in the group to read the book aloud to the group.
4. Discuss and evaluate the book based on the following questions:
   - Why did you select the book you did?
   - Have someone give a brief summary of the story.
   - Did you like the book? Why or why not?
   - For what age group is this book intended? Why?
   - Were the illustrations appropriate?
   - Would both boys and girls like this book?
   - When would this book be read to a child?
   - Does it present death as irreversible? Universal?
   - Did you read this book as a child? How old were you when you first read it? Do you remember your reaction?
   - What other evaluative comments do you have?

RECOMMENDED TERMS/ IMPORTANT PEOPLE/WEBSITES

Important People

Helen Harris, MSW. Senior Lecturer, School of Social Work. Baylor University.

National Hospice and Palliative Care Organization, www.nhpco.org

Books for children about death

Ages 4–8

John Adams. The Dragonfly Door. Revised 1st edition
Feather Rock Books. Maple Plain, MN. 2007.

Julie Kaplow, PhD and Donna Pincus, PhD. Samantha Jane's Missing Smile: A Story About Coping with the Loss of a Parent. Magination Press. *Washington, DC. May 2007.*

Joyce C. Mills, PhD Gentle Willow: A Story for Children About Dying. Magination Press. Washington, D. C. Second Edition, 2003. (For children who may not survive their illness or for children who are grieving.)

Cynthia Rylant. Dog Heaven. Blue Sky Press, New York, 1995.

Doris Stickney. Water Bugs and Dragonflies: Explaining Death to Young Children. Pilgrim Press Cleveland, OH. 1982

Melissa Wells. Remembering Ruby, for Families Living Beyond the Loss of a Pet. Outskirts Press. Denver, Colorago. August 2007. (This book contains a "Guide for Parents" section.)

Ages 8-adult

Clea Adams and John Adams. The Dragonfly Secret Feather Rock Books. Maple Plain, MN. October 2008.

Michael A. Carestio. Black Jack Jetty: A Boy's Journey Through Grief Magination Press. Washington, D.C. 2010.

Pat Scheweibert, Chuck Deklyen, Taylor Bills. Tear Soup. 3rd Revised edition, Grief Watch Publishing. Portland, OR. June 2005.

Wayne L. Wilson, *Kate,* Ghost Dog: Coping with the Death of a *Pet* Magination Press, Washington, D. C. 2009.

Teenagers

Earl Grollman Straight Talk About Death for Teenagers: How to Cope with Losing Someone You Love. Beacon Press. Boston, MA 1993.

Alan Wolfeldt. Healing Your Grieving Heart for Teens: 100 Practical Ideas. Companion Press. Fort Collins, CO. 2007.

NOTES

XI
Funerals and Body Disposition...
"Ashes to Ashes and Dust to Dust"

READ

<u>Funerals</u>

The expression of grief—mourning—is not only done in private, it is also ritualized in public. Gathering publically as a group of family and/or friends to observe the life of a person who has died is done most often in a funeral or memorial service. A funeral, where the deceased's body is present, or memorial service, where the deceased's body is not present, provides a socially acceptable means of expressing sorrow. A graveside service, which may be private-only for family or the actual service may be held by the grave, provides another option to express grief. Our society even encourages this public gathering of a community, and in many ways, expects it to take place.

There are many different expressions of sorrow, sadness, and even joy at a service of mourning, depending on the person's culture, religion, family, and community. A service can be long or short, religious or non-religious in nature, or be held at a cemetery. The range is from highly liturgical, religious services held at cathedrals that are sad and somber to small, intimate gatherings held at a park with laughter, stories, and children playing. Both, and most everything in between, are acceptable practices, with one's religious views often determining the type of service that takes place. It is the religious and philosophical context of the service that brings meaning and significance both to the life of the deceased, as well as to the lives of the mourners.

The most common elements of a funeral or memorial service may resemble each other, although the expression of them may differ greatly. Music is almost always an important part of the service, whether through singing, instrumental, or in electronic form. It often begins a service and then is interspersed throughout. Family members choose music based on their loved one's favorite song or favorite type of music. Music evokes emotions in us, and in this setting the mourners are given an acceptable time and place to express those emotions. In addition, a eulogy, a spoken tribute to the deceased, is offered; sometimes the obituary is read. The presiding clergy, a family member, or a friend may give the eulogy. If religious in nature, a brief sermon may also be given by the presiding clergy, a family member, or a friend. Following this, if the body is present, and if the family has chosen, those gathered at the service are guided to file by the body that is in the casket. A mourner may choose to do this or not. It is one way of "saying goodbye" to the one who has died; however, and perfectly acceptable, some families choose not to engage in this ritual.

Finally, if the body is present and is to be buried within driving distance, the funeral home employees see that the body is placed in a vehicle, either a hearse or a van, and driven to the place of burial for the interment. A familiar ritual is to see a cortege, or funeral procession, driving through towns and cities, perhaps across the countryside, en route to a final resting place.

While these common elements have composed funerals and memorial services for decades, in other ways, funerals have changed quite dramatically over the past century. In the early part of the twentieth century, funerals were more public. People died at home with the extended family and friends present. At that time, in what was most often rural communities, death was not feared, it was not closed off in institutions behind closed doors. It was part of the cycle of life that was lived out before one another. Families lived within close distances from one another. Adult children married and stayed close to the family farm and community. Women died in childbirth. Children died young. Infectious diseases were the culprits in quick deaths. Death was familiar. It happened at home. It was a family affair surrounded by the community.

In addition, the deceased's body was often "laid out" on the kitchen table, or on a table in the living area of the house. The community came by to pay their respects. Food was brought to the family and a vigil was kept by sitting with the deceased throughout the night. Funerals happened on family property at the grave that was dug by friends and family, or perhaps at the community church. The country church employed a person they called a "sexton." Their job was to ring the church bell for church services, weddings, and funerals. The sexton was also the church "property keeper." When a death occurred, they were responsible for opening and closing the grave site. The sexton is still used today at some community cemeteries. Funerals took place quickly because embalming did not normally take place.

Today's view of funerals paints quite a different picture. Funerals are not the family affair they once were. Most deaths take place in institutions like hospitals and nursing homes, not in homes. The funeral industry is now firmly rooted in our society. It has become a valuable and expected tool in the planning of funerals and body disposition. Whether humble or ornate, funeral homes offer their locations as places where the community pays its respect and holds vigil. Their chapels are open to holding funerals and memorial services, regardless of religion. They even assist families in arranging for the body disposition, whether it is in-ground burial or cremation. While they are both a service industry and a profit-making business, they are invaluable in their assistance to families.

On their website, the National Funeral Directors Association states the number of U.S. funeral homes in this country, listed in the National Directory of Morticians Redbook, to be approximately 19,486 in 2014. On the same website, it is estimated that the revenue of funeral homes and funeral homes combined with crematories will be $17.2 billion dollars by the year 2019. In addition, U.S. funeral homes employed 70,880 workers in 2013.

As costs for goods and services have risen in our country over the past 50 years, so have the costs for funerals. As you can see in Table 11.1 below, the average cost of a "basic" funeral today can be projected to be approximately $7,000 to $10,000 (with a vault, see Table 11.2). The vault price is listed separately because not every cemetery requires that a vault be used. They are not required items to be purchased, as a casket would be, unless the cemetery owners require them due to heavy settling of the soil in the cemetery. Vaults are outer containers made of heavy metal in which the casket is placed. Cremation costs can range from $500 to over $2000. (see Table 11.3) A funeral home is required by law to display the lowest and highest prices for their products.

TABLE 11-1   Average Cost of Adult Funeral Through the Years

YEAR	COST OF AN ADULT FUNERAL
1960	$708
1965	$790
1971	$983
1975	$1285
1980	$1809
1985	$2737
1991	$3742
1995	$4626
2000	$5180
2006	$6195
2009	$6,560
2012	$7,045

TABLE 11-2**   Itemized Funeral Costs 2013
The cost of a regular, adult funeral includes the following basic items. This does not include cemetery, monument/marker costs, or miscellaneous charges such as flowers or obituaries.

ITEM	PRICE
Non-declinable basic services fee	$1,975
Removal/transfer of remains to funeral home	$285
Embalming	$695
Other preparation of the body	$225
Use of the facilities/staff for viewing	$400
Use of facilities/staff for funeral ceremony	$495
Use of a hearse	$295
Use of a service car/van	$130
Basic memorial printed package	$150
Subtotal without Casket:	$4,650
Metal Casket	$2,395
Subtotal with Casket:	$7,045
Vault (may not be required)	$1,298
Total Cost:	**$8,343**

***2013 NFDA General Price List Survey.**

TABLE 11-3   Itemized Cremation Costs 2013

ITEM/SERVICE	MEDIAM CHARGE
Direct Cremation (no service): Includes crematory fee and alternative container*	$2,260
Cremation with memorial service (no viewing)	$3,250
Adult casket funeral with viewing and cremation*	$5,410
OTHER CREMATION CHARGES	
Urn*	$275
Cremation casket*	$995

The cost of cremation includes the following basic items. This does not include the columbarium at the cemetery, the columbarium marker, or miscellaneous charges such as flowers or the obituary.

*2013 NFDA General Price List Study

As noted in Table 11.2, these are basic costs that include services for employees, transportation, and use of the building. You will note that it costs more to use a traditional hearse than it does to use a van, an option that has become more common over the past few years. The basic cost in Table 11.2 includes a metal casket; however, caskets that are made from wood are more expensive which would increase the total cost. Another added cost includes flowers and an obituary, which as noted in the table heading, are not provided by the funeral home. The family pays separately for the obituary that is printed both in newspapers and in the electronic versions of newspapers. Other added costs include the cemetery plot, the opening and closing of the grave, statues, and the grave marker. Honorarium for the soloist, musician, and preacher will also be an extra cost. One does need to know that many funeral homes usually provide their goods and services at no cost for anyone who dies at age 18 or younger. What a blessing that is to the family!

A new item in a service that has grown popular over the past decade is that of showing a video of the deceased person's life at the funeral home. Some funeral homes have the technology to make a video from photographs submitted by the family. The video, which is usually in CD format, may be played during the visitation time, prior to the service, or during both times. Following the service, the funeral home will present the CD to the spouse or family. The funeral home may even have the technology to "live-stream" the service to military overseas or to out-of-state family. While the cost of the funeral increases with this tribute, it is a beautiful and simple way of adding depth to the deceased person's life.

There is another new item that is growing in popularity that involves the visitation or viewing time. During this time, families may choose to offer simple food like cookies, or fruit and cheese, or maybe even a favorite food of the deceased. This gesture hopes to provide a little comfort in the time of new grief. This is also a way to show appreciation to guests as they express their sympathy and respect for the deceased.

Another option is to have a luncheon, which is a more traditional event. This usually follows the service or interment. This may be provided by members of the church or by friends. The family home or a church fellowship hall are common places for this to take place. In some instances, there may even be a buffet following the service for all guests. Choosing to have a lunch or dinner with family and friends after the service will allow a time of visitation and a time to share special memories.

There are alternatives to a traditional funeral, of course. Some choose to have an immediate burial or cremation. This would simply take place within one or two days after the death. A memorial service may or may not be scheduled at a future date. Some families choose to have a small, brief family-only service at the graveside. Some desire a public memorial service to follow, either in a church or funeral home, others do not. The donation of one's body to a medical institution for anatomical study is another choice that people make. Medical institutions have procedures in place for this process which would require the family to be in contact with them before the death occurs.

Funerals are remarkable gatherings where past, present, and future are assembled. Family members of different generations congregate in one place to remember one person in their lives. Myriad feelings are brought into the service, and not all of them positive. However, it is a time when death is publically acknowledged; where the deceased's past is reviewed; and where the mourners, at least for a few moments, hear and think about not only the deceased's life, but their own lives, as well. It is a rare time when reflection on both death and life occur.

<u>Body disposition</u>

There are several methods of body disposition when deciding what happens to the deceased's body after death. In determining which method to select, the most important consideration is, "What did the deceased want?" This is a personal decision and hopefully was discussed prior to the loved one's death. If unable to have that conversation, families choose based on their knowledge of the deceased or on the family's traditions.

In-Ground Burial

In-ground burial is the most common and most traditional method of body disposition in the United States. It takes place at a gravesite or a plot in a cemetery. The cemetery is a burial ground that is either owned by a company or by a group of individuals. An in-ground burial requires a casket, sometimes called a coffin. The sexton is used to open and close the grave. The placing of the casket into the ground, or burial, is also called interment. A headstone or statue may be placed at the head end of the casket stating information about the deceased.

Above-Ground Burial

Above-ground burial may take place at a mausoleum, a building with burial chambers. The casket is positioned in the chamber, a drawer-like space, with plaques of personal information of the deceased being placed on the outside of the chamber. Mausoleums are also known as crypts or tombs.

Embalming

Embalming, the removal of the blood and replacement with a form-aldehyde-based fluid, is a process that may or may not be chosen by the deceased's family. The reasons one may choose to embalm is for preservation, disinfecting, and appearance of the body. This procedure is not a required state law, it is not essential, and it is an extra cost to the family, as indicated in Table 11.2. The difference of a good or bad funeral home is often rated according to the color of the deceased following the embalming process.

Cremation

Cremation is growing in popularity (see Table 11.4) and is the right choice for many people. Taking place inside a crematorium, which may or may not be part of a funeral home, cremation is the burning of a corpse at very high temperatures in order to reduce it to bone fragments that feel and look like ashes.

TABLE 11-4   Projected Comparison of Burials vs. Cremations

YEAR	PROJECTED BURIAL RATE	PROJECTED CREMATION RATE
2015	45.8%	48.2%
2020	38.1%	55.8%
2030	23.2%	70.6%
2015-Texas	50.1%	41.2%

2013 NFDA General Price List Study

The process begins as follows...

> *There is a waiting time of 48 hours before a cremation can take place. The casket (or casket-size box) is positioned in the cremation chamber that is set at a temperature of approximately 1400 to 1700 degrees Fahrenheit. If a person is large, the head is placed first into the chamber; but for a smaller person, the feet are placed in the the chamber first. After approximately two hours, the cremated remains are removed from the chamber, processed into fine particles, and then placed in a small container, such as an urn or box.*

After cremation has taken place, the family may choose to take the cremated remains, also known as cremains, with them and place in an urn to keep at home. Also, there are times when the family may choose to scatter the cremains or ashes in a spot that was special to the deceased. Cremains may not be thrown in populated areas. Another option is burying the remains in the ground in a cemetery, or placing the urn in a mausoleum or a columbarium. A columbarium is a place that is designated for the placement of the cremated remains of the dead. Columbaria are often found at churches, either indoors or outdoors. They contain niches in which urns of the cremated remains may be kept. As in mausoleums, names and personal information of the dead may be engraved on small plaques indicating where the remains are kept. The costs for cremation are in Table 11.3.

Other Options

There are, of course, less traditional ways of body disposition. The current green movement has suggestions that are earth-friendly. In addition, one website contains an article titled, "12 Weird Things to Do with Your Cremated Remains." It states that remains may be shot into space or made into diamonds (www.budgetlife.com). These options may be more expensive than burial or the simple scattering of remains, but if one has the financial means, then it's a sure way to be remembered.

Responsibilities of a funeral home director

We have learned how valuable funeral homes have become to our society as well as what our choices are in body disposition, but what about the actual position of the funeral home director? The director not only guides us in our choices and decisions for the service, but they provide that special attention we need in time of grief and mourning. They put our plan into action, they direct the service with utmost professionalism, and they even drive us to the cemetery. Their goal is to make a difficult time as memorable as possible for the deceased and the family. But when does this process start for the director? How does the director know when that special person dies and the family requests the use of their services and funeral home?

Following are the steps that are taken when they get that phone call:

1. 1st call

    This call may be from a hospital, a nursing home, hospice, Justice of the Peace, or a home. This call states that a death has occurred, the body is ready, and the family would like to use their service. Funeral homes are available 24/7 – 365 days a year.

2. Pick up the body

    Two people, a director and an assistant, will go to the place to pick up the body.

3. Ask family questions

    The funeral director will ask the family the following questions:
    a. What type of service would you like?
        (funeral? memorial? graveside?)
    b. What choice for body disposition?

4. Go back to funeral home

    Once they get back to the funeral home, they will begin the chosen body disposition. If cremation, the body will be placed in a refrigerated space until the proper paper work is approved.

5. Make an appointment

    The funeral director will call the family to set a time for them to come to the funeral home to plan the service.

6. Sit with the family

    The funeral director sits down with the family to make the arrangements for the service. The service includes the minister, music, possible video, cemetery, casket or urn, writing the obituary, and the number of death certificates.

7. Make the arrangements

    The funeral home director and employees will make the needed phone calls for the arrangements and service.

8. Setup for viewing/service

    If requested, the funeral home will set up for the visitation. This may be in the chapel or a viewing room. The service is also arranged.

9. Visitation and service

    The funeral director plus the assistants will coordinate and direct the service.

10. Cemetery-interment	The funeral director plus the assistants will transport the casket and family as they lead the processional to the cemetery. They will also transport the flowers and arrange them at the grave. If the family requested a police motorcycle escort, the police will lead the processional to the cemetery and the funeral director and assistants will meet at the cemetery to direct the interment.
11. Official paperwork	Following the interment, the director will provide the family with the official paperwork and the sympathy cards from the flowers. If appreciation cards were purchased, those will be in the package.
12. Following the service	The funeral director will complete a case report for each person who received their service.

Immediate questions for the spouse or family

After looking at the funeral director and their responsibilities, we need to take a look at the family side. With the death of a beloved family member, the family usually is in a state of shock even though it may have been an expected death.

We are never prepared for a death! When that death occurs, our mind is rolling with emotions and we usually cannot think about anything except the loss of our loved one. In the heat of strong emotions, there will be questions that must be answered by a spouse or family member at the time of the death. Except for those questions asked by the funeral director, the following questions should be considered:

- Who will you call first?
- Who else is on your list to contact?
- Who do you want to make those calls?
- How do you want to share the sad message?
- Who do you want to go with you to the funeral home?
- Who do you want to stay with you?
- What will the deceased want to wear?
- What will you wear to the service?
- Who will drive you to the service and back home?

These are all hard questions to think about now let alone while being burdened with grief. We just do not think well when we are grieving.

Thinking about these questions now can help one feel more prepared.

What to wear?

In looking at those immediate questions, "what to wear" can be challenging. We have all experienced a time when we looked in our closet, stared at our clothes, and asked ... "what am I going to wear? Our decision depends on the event, the time, the place, the weather, who will be with you, and how long you will be gone. Deciding what to wear to a funeral service is no different. In medieval times, people always wore black to a funeral. They believed that wearing black would hide the family and friends so the "spirit" could not recognize them and follow them home. Traditionally, black has always been worn to show grief and mourning. Wearing purple usually signifies royalty and white is worn for children's death. Today, people will wear any color. When a funeral is scheduled during the early afternoon, you might see an employee wear their uniform. This is so they can attend the service and then return to work quickly. In smaller country communities, people will wear their boots and cowboy hats. Of course, their hats are removed during the service. This often depicts the deceased's lifestyle. Some people will announce in the obituary to wear the favorite color of the deceased. With all this to say, the most important thing about a funeral is that "you go." Your presence at a funeral demonstrates that you love, care, and respect the deceased and their family.

Summary

From the past and how funerals have changed to choosing the type of service and planning the details, we know it involves decisions and answers during a time of grief. In knowing what it costs today, we know the expenses will only increase.

Understanding the choices in body disposition allows us to decide what will be right for us in our death. We do need to remember that it is best for us to let someone know our decisions and better yet, have them written down. Hopefully, we have gained respect for funeral homes and their directors. Understanding their responsibilities and knowing they strive to make the service as memorable as possible provides that support that we all need in the time of mourning. Knowing the possible questions allows us to be more prepared in a difficult and uncertain time. Funerals are a time to remember and honor the deceased with dignity and respect. Our hope is that it will tell a little bit about the story of our life.

REFLECT

Questions to guide your reflection:

*Have you ever helped to plan a funeral?

*What would your epitaph say?

> *For this reflection, draw your version of a tombstone.*
> *Draw it on an 8 ½ by 11 sheet of paper.*
> *Make the tombstone drawing large enough so that words can be written on it.*
> *On the tombstone, write your name and the epitaph you would like to have written. In other words, write what you would like to be remembered for.*
> *Following this exercise, write a one-page reflection on this experience.*
> *What was it like to think about what you want your life to be remembered for?*
> *What do you want your legacy to be and can that be stated on your epitaph?*

*What do you want your funeral to look like?

*Who do you want there?

*Do you know where you want to be buried? Or do you want to be cremated?

*Do you have anything special that you want said or done at your funeral?

Quotes to ponder:

"Live life fully … have no regrets … show honor … and be honored!"

"Once you accept the fact that you will die, you will be amazed at the life that you will live!"

"Death is an ending only for those of us who are still wrapped up in the story of our early lives."

REACT

Activity   *Cemetery Visit*

Instructions: Make a visit to a cemetery and answer the following questions.
The list below provides a space for you to record your information.
<u>Cemetery Visit Project:</u>
Must be typed!
#1 - #16: Type the number – Type the question- Type your answer
        (Do not need to use complete sentences…may list your answers)

#17: **New paragraph explaining "reflective feelings" you felt as you toured and completed the project?**

Optional: To include pictures

Due: _____

1. **Name and location** of cemetery … include city and state.
2. Describe the **"plot arrangements" that you observed.** *(How are grave sites organized?)*
3. What **directions** are the headstones facing *(north-south-east-west)*?
4. Describe, take pictures, or draw any **interesting headstones.**
5. What was the **deceased remembered for**? How do you **know**?
6. Look for any **interesting epitaphs** ….. *write at least 2 down.*
7. What **image or general belief** about "death" is presented?
8. See if you can find any tombstone for someone with the **same last name** as you. *(Option: Look for first name, too)*
9. Find the **"oldest birthdate."** Find the **"most recent"** death. *(include name & dates)*
10. What is the **"oldest Life span"** *(include name & dates)* that you can find?
11. What was the **"shortest life span"** *(include name & dates)* found on a marker?
12. What **interesting keepsake or sentimental trinkets** were left on the grave? *(Describe what you see)*
13. What type of **flowers** were left? Are they artificial or real? *(What kind & color)*
14. Are there any **above-ground mausoleums**? *(Describe what they look like)*
15. List or describe your **feelings while "in the cemetery."**
16. Other **thoughts or unique observations**?
17. Write a "reflective paragraph" … your **reactions and feelings you felt as you "prepared" this assignment.** *(Please underline your adjectives)*

Activity   *Visit A Funeral Home and Write a Reflection Paper*

Instructions: As a class or individually, make an appointment to visit a funeral home. Most funeral homes consider it part of their community service and public relations to give behind-the-scenes tours to local groups or individuals.

Following the tour, submit a reflection paper on your funeral home experience. Include descriptive words or adjectives to describe your thoughts and feelings. What did you observe about yourself, your classmates, and the professional who was your tour guide? Did memories of past times in funeral homes come to your mind? Were you anxious or afraid? Remember to give a reflection not a summary.

The Tour: *Note: The tour may not go in the exact order. The tour may not be able to observe all areas due to a possible death.

Listed below are possible areas that may be observed on the tour.
There is a column to record information and a column for your feelings?
This is provided to help you in the reflection process.

Reflection Due: _____

Date of Tour:_____

Name of Funeral Home: _____

Area	Information	Your Feelings?

Entrance/Foyer:

Planning Room:

Visitation/Viewing:

Chapel:

Embalming Room:

Crematory:

Hearse:

Luncheon / Reception:

Other Notes/Comments:

Activity: *Write Your Own Obituary*

Instructions: Write your obituary as if you have lived to be: **<u>80 YEARS OLD</u>**
Suggestions:
Go to current newspaper websites in the section to see examples.
When you have your obituary written...*READ OUT LOUD* to see how it sounds.
*Note of Explanation: If any "special situations" need defined, please include a note at top of assignment.

Due: _____

Title on Obituary:	Full Name? Date of Birth? – Date of Death?
1st Paragraph:	**Provides information on the death and the service.** Full name of person who died? City - State - Place of death? Visitation: Date/Place/Time? Service: Date/Place/Time? Type of service: funeral?/memorial?/graveside? Interment: what cemetery/when? Clergy?
2nd Paragraph:	**Provides the background information of the deceased.** Where born? Parents? Where raised? High School? College-University Attended /Degrees? Occupation / Where you worked? Religious Affiliation? Military Service? Membership in organizations? Community contributions? Any interesting facts or hobbies?
3rd Paragraph:	**Provides family information on who preceded the deceased in death.** Parents: Father's / Mother's name? Spouse? *(Note: spouse may have preceded the death)* *(include maiden name for women)*
4th Paragraph:	**Provides family information on who survived the deceased in death.** Marital Status? *(Note: spouse may have preceded the death)* Spouse's name? *(include maiden name for women)*

| | Children? | Daughter plus *(if married)* her husband's name *(son-in-law)*? Son plus *(if married)* his wife's name *(daughter-in-law)*? Where they live: name/city/state? |

Children? Daughter plus *(if married)* her husband's name *(son-in-law)*?
Son plus *(if married)* his wife's name *(daughter-in-law)*?
Where they live: name/city/state?

Grandchildren?
Great Grandchildren? *(names or just say number of great-grandchildren)*
Sisters / Brothers? Possible husband/wife of each?
Where they live: name/city/state?
Any other family or special people?

5ᵗʰ Paragraph: **Provides any extra information.**
Pallbearers? or Honorary Pallbearers?
Possible memorials or donations? *(include address for mailing)*
If in lieu of flowers…what do you want?
May include a brief statement about the deceased's life?
Any special instructions when attending the service or interment?
Any "thank you's" *(hospital – hospice –doctor's etc.)?*
Website guestbook?

Activity: ***Plan Your Own Funeral***

Instructions: Completely plan your funeral based on your death occurring while you are a college student.
Plan as if your death occurred:_____
Type the number/letter, then your answer.
For "non-applicable" answers, use: NA
Be specific in your answer! May list your answers.
*I should be able to plan your funeral using your information provided!
*Note of Explanation: If any "special situations" need defined, please include a note at top of assignment.
Due:_____
Title: Full Name?
Birth Date - Death Date?
Date of Service?
1. **Funeral Home or Crematory?** *Choose "A" or "B" or Both "A & B"*
   A. Name of Funeral Home:_____
      City:_____State:_____
   B. Name of Crematory:_____
      City:_____State:_____

C. I want my body transported to the funeral home in a _____.

D. Why did you choose this/these particular place(s) to take care of your body?

2. **Body Disposition?**

   A. I would like my "final body disposition" to be _____.

   Choices: any of the following that applies to what you want done ....
   Embalmed - Cremation- Donated to Science

   B. What influenced your decision?

3. **What will you wear?**

   (*Even if you are cremated or donated to science ... .answer this question)

   (Clothes – jewelry – makeup –hair, etc?)

4. **Container?** *Choose "A," "B," or "C"*

   A. If *Embalmed:*

      1. What casket? *(Describe kind, color, markings, lining etc. or include picture)*

      2. Cost of casket:_____

   B. If *Cremated:*

      1. What urn or container: *(Describe the urn/container or may include picture)*

      2. Cost of urn:_____

   C. *If Embalmed – Viewed – then Cremated:*

      1. What casket? *(Describe kind, color, markings, lining etc or include picture)*

      2. Casket: Rent or Buy?

      3. What urn or container? *(Describe the urn/container or include picture of urn)*

      4. Cost of casket:_____

         Cost of urn:_____

5. **Burial?** *Choose "A" or "B"*

   A. *Casket:*

      1. I would like my casket to be buried: Gravesite plot or Mausoleum?

      2. Vault required? Yes or No

      3. Name of cemetery: _____

         City: _____ State:_____

      4. Why did you choose this cemetery?

   B. *Urn/Container: Answer #1 or #2 or Both plus #3*

      1. Burial:

         a. Name of Cemetery/Columbarium

         b. City:_____ State:_____

      2. Ashes Thrown:

         a. Place? *(* be specific – state?- ocean? - mountains – etc.?)*

         b. Why do you want your ashes thrown at this particular place?

      3. Other Options: ashes in necklaces/gems, etc.

6. **Grave Marker for Casket or Urn?**

   A. Full Name

   B. Birth Date to Death Date

   C. Any epitaph?

7. **Flowers?** *Choose A or B or Both A and B*
   A. *If you want flowers?*
      1. Any special kind? Color?
      2. Do you want a "floral spray" for your casket?
   B. *If you request NO flowers?*
      1. Do you want special donations? Yes or No?
      2. If "yes, donations can be made to ____?
      3. Address where to make donation?
      4. Why did you choose this/these donation choices?
8. **Visitation ("Wake" or "Viewing")?**
   A. "Yes" or "No"
   B. When will the visitation take place? *(Date – Day – Time?)*
      Choices: Day/evening before service –On same day immediately prior to service
   C. Visitation will take place at the _____?
      Choices: Funeral home –Church – Home - "Viewed at funeral home, then cremated"?
   D. Name and address of where visitation will take place? *(City/State)*
   E. Do you want casket: Opened or closed?
9. **Service?**
   A. 1. My service will be a _____.
         Choices: Funeral Service –Memorial Service – Graveside (may choose 1 or all 3
      2. If no service, state "why."
   B. 1. I want my service to be _____. *(Religious? or Secular?)*
      2. Why did you choose this type of service?
   C. 1. I want my service to be held _____.
         Choices:
         Church - Chapel in Funeral Home – Cemetery - or a special place
      2. Name and address *(City/State)* of chosen place *(your answer in C1)*
   D. Casket or Urn at your service?
      1. Casket or Urn present? "Yes" or "No"
      2. Casket opened or closed? Which part of the service?
      3. Why did you make this decision?
   E. People / Events I want in my service?
      1. **Pallbearers?** *(to carry casket or urn)*
         a. Yes or No?
         b. Who do you want to carry your casket *(need at least 6)* or urn?
         c. Why did you choose these people?
      2. **Processional** of family at the beginning of the service?
         a. Yes or No?
         b. Do you want the casket or urn included in the processional?
         c. Why do you want a processional?
      3. **Lead person** – Introduces speakers, etc? *(can be minister or special person)*
         a. Who do you want to be the leader of your service?
         b. Why did you choose this particular person?

4. **Music?**
   a. Yes or No?
   b. Name of songs-music/artist you want played?
   c. How performed? *(CD, piano, guitar, orchestra, etc)*
   d. Names of the musicians you need?
   e. Any special reason you selected this music?
5. **Soloist, Duet, Trio or Choir**
   a. Yes or No?
   b. Name of soloist / duet / trio / choir? *(include names of those you chose)*
   c. Name of the songs/artist you want sung?
   d. How performed? *(CD, guitar, piano, etc.)*
   e. Musicians needed for soloist /duet trio / choir?
   f. Why did you choose these people?
6. **Scripture Reader?**
   a. Yes or No?
   b. Name of person to read the scripture?
   c. Bible /scripture verse to read?
   e. Any special reason why you want this scripture read?
7. **Reader of Eulogy?**
   a. Yes or No?
   b. Who will read?
   e. Why did you choose this person?
8. **The Message?** *(Can be the leader, a pastor, or another person)*
   a. Yes or No?
   b. Who will deliver message?
   c. Why did you choose this person?
9. **Any Special Speakers?**
   a. Yes or No?
   b. Who?
   c. Why do you want this special speaker?
   d. What do you want them to do in your service?
10. **Any Special Quotes or Stories** to include?
    a. Yes or No?
    b. Write the quote or include story?
    c. Who will read or tell the quote or story?
    d. Why is this special?
11. **Recessional?**
    a. Yes or No?
       Choices: *1) At the end of service, people file by the family and then casket or urn to pay respect?*
       2) Casket or Urn is carried by pallbearers with family following?
    b. If answer is "Yes," what is your choice? *(#1#, #2 or something different?)*
    c. Why?

10. **Interment?**
    A. When do you want the interment?
       Choices: Before service – Following service – At a later date
    B. Where?
    C. How do you want your casket or urn transported? *(hearse – carriage – ?)*
    D. Who do you want to attend? "Private family only" or "Guest welcomed"?
    E. Police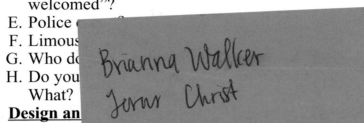
    F. Limous
    G. Who d
    H. Do you   ent? Who?
       What?

11. **Design an**   **for your service.**
12. **Other Op**
    A. Food or
       1. Yes
       2. If ye
    B. Lunch/R
       Choices   *interment or*

                                                     interment or

       1. Yes or
       2. Which choice?
       3. Where will it be held?
       4. Why do you want your choice?
    C. Video?
       1. "Yes" or "No"
       2. Any special pictures you want included?
       3. Why?
       4. When do you want the video shown?
          Choices: Visitation? – Before service? – Reception?
    D. Display Items?
       1. Yes or No?
       2. Picture /Special item?
       3. Where do you want it displayed?
       4. When do you want them displayed?
    E. Any other "Special Requests"? Be specific?
13. **I would prefer to leave the arrangements for my service to**

    _____.
    Why?
14. **Notification of Death - Obituary?**
    A. Newspaper? *(name of newspaper)*
    B. Other announcements: technology?

15. **Estimated Cost?**
    Figure the approximate cost of your funeral...include the following:
    A. Price range?
    B. Cost of the following: (*If this is a package deal...list package cost plus the extras)*
       Make a chart listing: Item and cost
       Death Certificates (*Include the number you want and the total cost*)
       Professional service charges (*List what these services include*)
       Embalming/ Cremation...cosmetology
       Visitation/Viewing
       Funeral service – Memorial service – graveside service?
       Transfer of remains (*moving body place to place- use of hearse – limo, police escort, etc.*)
       Burial acknowledgment – cards, programs. Thank you's .... etc.
       Cemetery Plot/Columbarium
       Police Escort
       Casket / Urn
       Burial (*opening/closing*)
       Vault
       Graves Marker
       Statue (optional)
       Obituary
       Flowers
       TOTAL COST?

16. **Reflective feelings as you planned and made your decisions and choices?**
    1. Explain any class information/experiences that influenced your choices?
    2. Are your decisions and choices different from what you thought you would make before this class?
       Explain why?
    3. Describe your feelings you felt as you prepared and wrote your funeral plan.
       Be sure to include your thoughts and feelings about all the people involved.
       Underline your adjectives.

Activity   *Attending Your Own Funeral*

Instructions: Room: arranged where participants can lie comfortably on their backs not touching other participants.
                    Time: 1-1 ½ hours
                    State the following instructions, ***pausing after each statement.***
    1. Lie on your back, legs uncrossed, close your eyes (ones wearing contacts may want to remove them).
    2. Make yourself as comfortable as you can.
    3. Let all the events and worries of the day roll around in your mind.
    4. When you are ready, leave all those thoughts behind.

5. Appreciate the peacefulness.
6. Pay attention to the places on your body that feel tense.
7. Take a deep breath,,hold it, let it out slowly to a count of 5.
8. Let your breath go to abdominal breathing.
9. You are in complete control of your imagination now.
10. Follow along with what I am going to say as long as you are willing.
11. Let your body go.
12. Imagine that your life is gone. You do not speak or move.
13. You have died, and your funeral is about to take place.
14. You are now going to your own funeral.
15. Look at the people who have come to your funeral. What do they feel?
16. How did they look at your body?
17. Do they need consoling?
18. Are they happy to be alive?
19. What are their emotions?
20. Look at the people coming to say their last goodbye to you.
21. Is there one among them to whom you would like to say something to–explain something - or express a certain feeling?
22. You cannot do it...!
23. You do not have the power to talk, to write, or to move.
24. Look again at the people who attend your funeral.
25. What would you like to say to each of them?
26. What is the look on their face?
27. How would your express yourself to them if you could speak?
28. Do you have a problem that has been difficult to solve?
29. Do you have a decision that has been difficult to make?
30. Did you look at the flowers? Who sent them? What kind are they? What color?
31. Is anyone giving the eulogy? What is he or she saying?
32. Does it seem to you to be sensible and true about you?
33. Is there music? What kind?
34. Has someone chosen it who knew what you liked?
35. Now turn your attention to the person whom you disliked or irritated you.
36. Is there anything you want to say to that person?
37. And now look at the ones you love the most…imagine saying whatever you feel like saying.
38. This is your last party!
39. Speak to everyone there – tell them all about yourself – about your mistakes – about your love – and your longings.
40. No longer do you need to protect yourself – no longer do you need to hide.
41. At your funeral you can be yourself.

From *Thanatopics: Activities and Exercises for Confronting Death* by J. Eugene Knott, Mary C. Ribar, Betty M. Duson, Marc R. King. Copyright © 1991 by J. Eugene Knott, Mary C. Ribar, Betty M. Duson, Marc R. King. Reprinted by permission of the author.

42. Now it is over – come back to your living body.
43. Acknowledge and respect it. . Feel the life flowing in it. Feel your heart beat.
44. Notice your breathing.
45. When you are ready, let your attention come back to this room.
46. Now, I am going to count backwards slowly from 5 to 1. When I reach 1, I want you to open your eyes and you will feel alert and rested. 5…4…3…2…1
47. Open your eyes – sit up – look around you.

Reflective questions:

1. What was the experience like for you?
2. Would you like to share any part of your fantasy?
3. Was there any part of your fantasy that was especially meaningful to you?
4. What part was the most difficult?
5. Did you discover anything about your preferences regarding your funeral?
6. Did anything about the way you are living your life become clearer to you?
7. Did you experience any realizations about the persons in your life?
8. Did you discover any unfinished business that you might like to pursue at this time?

RECOMMENDED TERMS/ IMPORTANT PEOPLE/WEBSITES

Terms

Cremation: The burning of a corpse at very high temperatures in order to reduce the body to bone fragments.

Cremains: Cremated remains.

Crematory: The furnace where cremation takes place.

Columbarium: A place that is designated for the placement of the cremated remains of the dead.

Embalm: The process of removing the blood from a dead person's body and replacing it with a formaldehyde-based fluid.

Eulogy: A spoken tribute to the deceased given at a funeral or memorial service.

Funeral: A gathering of people for the purpose of observing the life of a person who has died and where the deceased's body is present.

Interment: Placing of the casket in the ground, the burial.

Mausoleum:	A building with burial chambers where caskets containing the dead are placed. Mausoleums are also known as crypts or tombs.
Memorial service:	The same as a funeral except that the deceased's body is not present at the service.

Websites

National Funeral Directors Association: www.nfda.org

Interesting Facts from the National Funeral Directors Association

Employment: U.S. funeral homes employed 102,877 workers in 2007.

Funeral home/funeral home combined with crematories revenue: $11.95 billion in 2007, increased from $11.05 billion in 2002.

Number of U.S. funeral homes (per office of *National Directory of Morticians Redbook*) 2010: 19,902; 2005: 21,495; 2000: 22,107.

NOTES

XII
Grief – Bereavement – Mourning…
"It's about remembering"

READ

<u>What is grief?</u>
Grief is the intellectual, emotional, physical, and spiritual response to a loss.

While grief can be experienced in various types of losses, such as a divorce or the loss of a job, here it will be addressed as the response to the death of a person.

While grief is natural and normal, it is helpful to know just what natural and normal means. Because each person's experience of grief can be different, and usually is, it does not mean that someone's experience is abnormal, wrong, or bad simply because it is different from another's.

Intellectual responses to grief may include thoughts that present themselves as denial, "It can't be true," or bargaining, "If only God would bring her back, I will give all my money to help the poor."

There are emotional responses such as sadness, guilt, depression, and loneliness. All of these are normal feelings during a time of grief. Anger is another common emotion—anger at the one who died, anger at oneself, or simply angry in general.

167

Physical responses, which often get overlooked as being a part of grief, include shortness of breath, sighing, nausea, muscle weakness, changes in appetite, fatigue, and insomnia.

Some people who experience grief may behave in ways that are curious, like daily visiting the gravesite of their loved one for months. They may call the loved one's phone number, expecting him or her to answer. They may sleep more than usual, or as mentioned above, not sleep much at all. They may withdraw socially, not attending events that they had regularly attended prior to the loved one's death.

Finally, people often have spiritual responses that surprise them. They may question their belief in all that they had believed in until this death. They may express anger at God or at others who represent God or their beliefs. This is often experienced as a type of spiritual crisis following a death.

A Summary of Grief

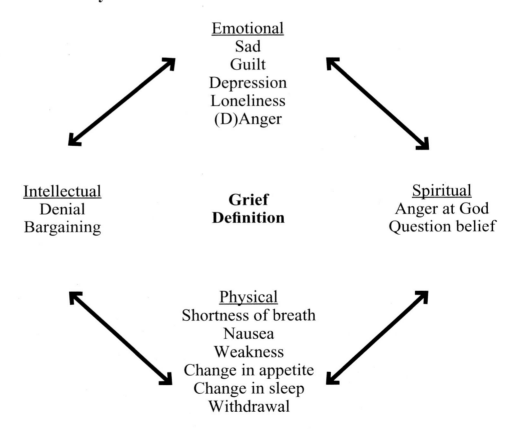

Examining the definition of grief helps us to know and recognize our own symptoms and responses as well as others. Because we can recognize that grief is a normal and natural response in our life, is there a good time to work on grief? Yes, the best work on grief is done way before a death occurs or a life crisis happens. At times, life can be challenging and throw us a hard blow. The more we understand what is happening in those responses, the more prepared we will be confront those challenges each day.

The responses that we experience during periods of grief move back and forth, as in a cycle.

Perhaps, though, the most important thing to remember about the grief experience is that one has to go through it. Just like the children's game that says, "...can't go under it...can't go over it...can't go around it... have to go through it." This is a description of the grief process.

The Cycle of Grief

Making Sense and Moving Forward

Shock and Confusion

Anger and Depression

Sadness and loneliness

Yearning

Anger, Depression, and Anxiety

Describing the cycle of grief

At the time of death, there is almost always numbness, shock, and confusion. One simply cannot grasp what has happened, shutting down from feeling anything except numbness. It does not process pain. One's body goes through familiar motions. Tears may be shed or may not be shed, but experiencing one and not the other is no indication of the amount of sadness or grief that is being felt. It does not mean that one is right and one is wrong. It is simply how one's body and mind are responding. This shock and numbness are nature's way of giving protection from the pain that is coursing through at the time.

Often what comes next—are anger and depression as the reality of the loss begins to be felt. After the numbness and shock wear off, one begins to deeply feel all that was not felt earlier. Pain is expressed by anger and depression. These emotions are like a roller coaster with highs and lows, but they are neither thrilling nor exciting. One day angry, the next day depressed. One week angry, two weeks depressed. This period is when people can be heard to say, "I feel like I am going crazy." Those who grieve are not going crazy. They are simply grieving.

Sadness and loneliness set in on the heels of the more volatile emotions. Exhausted from the anger and depression, one may find that sadness and loneliness have pervaded one's life. Closely accompanying this may be one's yearning for their loved one. Hearing their voices, dreaming, feeling their presence...yearning is a most powerful experience that brings comfort to some but disturbance to others.

The cycle then may shift on to the familiar territory of anger and depression again. They are close friends who never seem to be far away during these months of bereavement.

With the help of supporting family, friends, and community, the grieving person knows, though, that this is part of the process.

While the clouds of anger, depression, and sadness may linger for longer than we expect, there will be a day when a sliver of sun may peek through. Along with it is a glimpse of hope that whispers, "maybe, just maybe, I will not feel like this forever." However, a grieving person may have difficulty in moving forward. They may think, "If I feel better, does this mean that I have forgotten?" "Am I betraying my loved one by feeling better?" "Shouldn't I still feel sad?"

Again, it is helpful to remember that these thoughts are normal. It takes time for the mind and body to establish equilibrium. Over time, one's body and mind will have more and more moments of feeling, acting, and thinking in ways that are familiar.

Another way to look at stages of death is through the book, *On Death and Dying* by Elisabeth Kübler-Ross. We are all familiar with Kübler-Ross and her five stages of grief: *denial – anger – bargaining – depression – acceptance*. We can easily remember these stages by thinking of an acronym "DABDA." The five stages of grief not only applies in death, but can also be useful in our life relationships.

<u>Is there an end to grief?</u>

The question is often asked, "How long does it take to grieve?" An answer might be, "It takes as long as it takes." It is not uncommon for someone to still exhibit feelings and behaviors of grief for up to two years. This sounds like a long time, but the first six to nine months are spent being in shock and going through the motions of taking care of the "after death business." This time begins at the moment of death and includes the business of planning and going through the funeral, probating the will, and other legal matters that have their own time frame. It has been observed that at approximately nine to 12 months into one's period of grief, the pain will perhaps be at its greatest. The shock and numbness have worn off and the reality has become, in short, real. Following this, a person will walk through the labyrinth of grief that, over time and with support from a caring family and community, will take them to a place of peace.

The Duration of Grief

- ‣ Event
- ‣ 6 months...Shock fades, beginning to feel
- ‣ 9-12 months…Pain is greatest
- ‣ 12 months...Pain may worsen
- ‣ 18 months...Beginning to acclimate
- ‣ 2 years...The Road to Recovery

Grief reaction in types of death

Grief and Anticipatory Death

Anticipatory death occurs when someone has a prolonged illness. The patient, as well as family and friends, knows that death is just around the corner. Anticipating the death of a loved one is a natural process in the course of grief and mourning. As painful as it might be, planning for and expecting a death allows for the family or friends to slowly prepare for the reality of the death. People are often able to express their feelings of loss, or complete any "unfinished business" with the dying person . For example, anticipatory mourning can be expressed by saying, "I love you," or "I forgive you."

Example: Terminal Illness
Level of Grief: Least traumatic

Grief and Sudden Death

Sudden death is one that enters our life quickly. As opposed to anticipatory grief, the grief experienced after a sudden and unexpected death can be bewildering and overwhelming. The grief that emerges from sudden death can leave a person unable to function, with the impact and reality of the loss taking longer to comprehend than in an expected loss. It may also take longer to re-engage in the normal processes of daily living

Examples: Suicide, Disasters, Accidents, Heart Attack
Level of Grief: Very traumatic

Grief and Traumatic Deaths

During the period of grief that follows traumatic deaths such as disasters, some common questions might be, "Why did this happen?" "What is happening in the world?" "How do I cope?" "How do we go on?" "Are my feelings normal?" Many people have been touched by natural disasters, such as earthquakes and hurricanes, or by man-made disasters, such as war and the September 11, 2001, terrorist attacks.

The ranges of emotion experienced are normal reactions to very unusual and abnormal events. Some of the normal reactions might include:

1. Lack of focus
2. Difficulty with appetite and sleeping
3. Headaches and fatigue
4. Feelings of fear, guilt and anxiety
5. Nightmares and dreams

Complicated Grief

There are situations when the grief from a death may not develop in a normal manner. Sometimes an experience of grief may be so intense and so persistent that it interferes with a person's daily life, sometimes leaving a person unable to function. This time may be accompanied by extended periods of depression and anxiety. It is in these circumstances when help from a qualified professional may be recommended, for complicated grief rarely subsides on its own.

> Examples: Suicide, Disaster, Homicide
> Level of Grief: Traumatic Grief

What is bereavement?

Bereavement can be defined as:
> *"The period after a loss during which grief is experienced and mourning occurs."*
> *"A normal response and condition to being deprived of someone valued..as in the occurrence of a death."*
> *"A state of sorrow over the death or departure of a loved one."*

What can we do for the bereaved?

Consider these suggestions for ways to support *family or friends* who are grieving:
- Acknowledge all feelings and do not pass judgment on how well one is getting through their daily life. There is no right or wrong way to grieve.
- Be aware that there may be cultural or religious perspectives that are different from your own; the grieving person must take ownership of his or her personal beliefs and practices.
- Be willing to stay in relationship with the grieving person for an extended time. Others may withdraw and you will be needed.
- Be specific in your offer to help. For example, "I will bring dinner to your house on Saturday night. Is 6:00 a convenient time?" This is better than saying, "Let me know if you need something."
- Be mindful of holidays and other special days. For example, the first anniversary of the loved one's death looms as the day approaches; the first birthday following the loved one's death is

a special day to be remembered. No phone call, card, or other acknowledgment is too small when it comes to remembering someone who has died.

Consider these suggestions for ways to support *yourself* when you are the person who is grieving:
- Educate yourself about the grief process.
- Share your feelings with family and friends; don't keep them to yourself.
- Attempt to commit to the following approach: "I am adjusting to the new. I am going to get through this."
- Talk positive to yourself… be your own best friend.
- Talk to at least 3 people each day…. isolation will allow grief to deepen.
- Attempt to accept what cannot be changed; try to search for some kind of meaning in death.
- Find a new purpose in your life.
- Be easy on yourself when you have a bad day.
- Allow memories to surface … they will always be a part of you.
- Write your feelings in a journal.
- Let friends help you.
- Get plenty of rest.
- Eat nutritiously and exercise regularly.

So what is mourning compared to grief?
Mourning can be defined as the:
- *Process of feeling or expressing deep grief or sorrow.*
- *Period of exhibition or symbols that represent the grief for a person's death.*
- *Integration of the loss into everyday life.*

Examples: Wearing black
                   A team or organization wearing a special ribbon or armband

These symbolic examples represent the sorrow and grief that is felt for the loss as well as for the memory of that person who has died.

Following a death, the common expression that we hear is that a person is grieving, not mourning. Grieving and mourning go hand in hand, but because of our short style of funeral and memorial services, we tend to use the word grieving more. In the past, people may have been in mourning for a whole year by wearing black to symbolize to their friends and community that they were still observing their loss. Today, we do not see this as often, but what we do see is mourning being expressed to the community and world when, for example, an athletic team has lost one of its members, like the loss of an Olympic team member or basketball player. As the public views a competition following the death, we will see special armbands, or pieces of cloth, or the team member's jersey number, that is worn by each current team member to show that they are in mourning.

<u>Summary</u>

Whether we call it grief or mourning, or whether we are walking through the bereavement period, we know that the response is definitely real; we know that it can be short or long, that it can be emotional and physical, and that time can be a balm to the healing process. We are unique individuals who respond in unique ways, regardless of the type of experience. Those who grieve need to receive support as memories are held dearly, and life attempts to get back to normal.

Grief—"it's about remembering."

REFLECT

Questions to guide your reflection:

In a time of grief, it is often what is NOT said that is more helpful than what is said. The "Ministry of Presence" is one term. "Being there" is another term. Very often, people who are grieving do not remember words that someone said to them, but they indeed remember who was present for them.

Spend a few minutes reflecting on this gesture of being present for someone in a time of grief.

*Where does the urgency come from to say something profound?

*When was there a time in your life when someone's presence was meaningful to you?

*Why was this person's presence more meaningful than the words he or she spoke?

Quotes to ponder:

"You don't have to do something….simply be there."

"You do not have to apologize for grief."

"Longing will never go away. God keeps that spot empty on purpose."

"The pain of loss reflects how deeply our hearts have loved."

"Truly great friends are hard to find, difficult to leave, and impossible to forget."

REACT

Activity   *What You Always Wanted to Know About Grief but Were Afraid to Ask*

› Grief resurrects grief.
› Time changes.
› The process of grief and mourning takes longer than anyone can ever say.
› The pain never goes away....it changes, but doesn't leave.
› Grief is a lonely experience.

Instructions: (Large group)
  1. Look at the list of statements above.
  2. Reflect on one of the sentences in the list.
     • What drew you to this particular sentence?
     • What does this sentence say to you?
     • What experience of grief have you had?
  3. Divide into small groups of four.
  4. Share individual answers to number 2.
  5. From your own experiences, what would you add to this list?
  6. Small groups share with class and compile answers.

Activity   *What to Say and What NOT to Say*

What NOT to Say

• *It's been over a month...aren't you over it by now?*
• *You're young...you'll marry again ...you'll have another baby.*
• *I know just how you're feeling.*
• *God must have needed her more than you did.*
• *God needed another flower in His garden.*
• *Other?*

So... What Do I Say?

› "I'm sorry."
› Send a card.
› "I'm going to bring you dinner on Friday... is 6:00 a good time?"
   "Tell me about your mother."
   "Go ahead and cry."

Instructions: Review:
During times of grief, it is helpful to hear encouragement and words of comfort. However, not all words are comforting to those who are grieving. There are some words that are better left unsaid. It is good to give some thought to this ahead of an occasion when it might be needed.

Activity 1:
1. Make two lists on a sheet of paper.
2. Title one list, "What to Say" and the other, "What NOT to Say."
3. See lists in this activity for examples.
4. Add five or more of your own to these existing lists.
5. Have you had any of these words spoken to you?
6. Share your lists in either small group or large group.

Activity 2:
1. Listed below are five categories of "Grief Cliches" (with examples).
2. Underneath each category, list two to three clichés.
3. Discuss in small group or in large group.

Grief Cliches:
Be Strong   e.g., "Big boys don't cry."
Hurry Up   e.g., "You're not your old self."
Guilt   e.g., "Count your blessings."
God   e.g., "God needs him more than you do."
Discount   e.g., "I know just how you feel."

Activity   *Invite a Class Speaker*

Instructions: Invite a speaker from the community to speak to the class on his or her personal experience of grief and loss. Types of grief and loss experienced might be:
  • Spouse
  • Child
  • Parent
  • Suicide, e.g., elderly, teenager
  • Disaster, e.g., natural or man-made
  • Sudden or traumatic loss, e.g., homicide or accidental

Activity   *How to Help During the Holidays*

Instructions: 1. Ask each student to make a list of five ways to help a grieving person or family during the holidays.
2. Divide the class into groups of four.
3. Ask students to share their lists with the group.
4. Ask each group to share their lists with the entire class.

RECOMMENDED TERMS/IMPORTANT PEOPLE/WEBSITES

Important People

Elizabeth Kübler-Ross (July 8, 1926 – August 24, 2004) was a Swiss-born psychiatrist who authored the groundbreaking book, *On Death and Dying(1969)*. She is the expert whose "Stages of Grief" have been most widely accepted as the reference to grief and bereavement. These stages have been the starting point for subsequent models.

Louis LaGrand, Ph.D., is a grief counselor and the author of eight books. His most recent book is titled: *Love Lives On*: Learning from the Extraordinary encounters of the Bereaved. He is known for his research on bereavement experiences and is one of the founders of Hospice of the St. Lawrence Valley, Inc.

Websites

www.nhpco.org-National Hospice and Palliative Care Organization

Twelve Practical Tips for Saying, Doing the Right Things"
   National Hospice Foundation and the National Hospice and Palliative Care Organization

NOTES

XIII
Hope on the Journey...
"The gift of living life"

READ

A rainbow is full of colors blended together with overlapping shades. Some may see the rainbow as a mystical arch radiating across the sky, and others may see it as a promise of hope from God. So are our lives shaded and blended with the colors of our obstacles, struggles, decisions, accomplishments, and relationships that help to shape who we are. As the rainbow fades from end to end, so our lives fade from birth to death.

Hope

When considering death, the virtue of hope is part of our reflection as we look into the mystery. There is no exception to death. It is going to happen, we just do not know when. Simply reading the question...Is there hope in death?...and saying it aloud brings difficult questions that will never cease until the moment of death. There is a type of hope that we call upon when we initially receive bad news. It is the hope for a cure, the hope for physical healing. We pray for this, ask our doctors for this, and with all of the bargaining that we can muster, we hope for the fatal prognosis to disappear. Our emotions may be like a roller coaster from day to day. Both sincerity and doubts about our faith come bubbling to the surface. Questions about treatments, about the best places for treatments, about the best medicine, and about the best doctors swirl in our heads like a swarm of gnats. Our emotions entwine with this hope that we will live. While we know that hope cannot cure, we do know that hope can give us encouragement that is needed to cope at the end of life.

Another type of hope is one that calls for wholeness. This difficult issue of hope and healing moves from being an intellectual matter to being existential as we face the reality of our death. This is hope that encompasses the physical, emotional, and spiritual components of who we are. This hope is one for healing in a different sense. It is a healing that goes beyond our bodies, calling on our resources of trust and belief in what is not seen. It is desire outside of the physical realm, a synthesis of all that we have gathered to this point in our lives. Not only in our imagination, but also in the living out of our last days, we hope for freedom from not only physical suffering, but of any type of emotional or spiritual suffering. We long for forgiveness, we desire to embody peace, we cherish each brush of a kiss against our skin, and we embrace each touch of a hand. Gazes grow long and smiles turn into never-forgotten memories. We gain this hope not only through our own inner resources and our own efforts, but also through others. None of this happens in isolation, but only with the help of others who love us and care for us. Often when we are depleted of all that we know as hope, others will remind us that we are not alone, and somehow that can make all the difference. To use part of the adage, *it takes a village* to help people live well and *it takes a village* to help people die well. The patient is not "giving up," but instead is going down the path to resolution and peace.

Summary of hope

Happening   **O**pportunity   **P**ossibility   **E**ncouragement

What is hope?

Fulfillment of one's desires
Confident assurance
Inspiration of faith
The most precious treasure
   to a person
Anticipation of receiving
   goodness

What does hope do?

Looks for the good in people
Opens doors
Discovers what can be done to
   help
Sets people free
Lights a candle

Our faith, virtue, and wholeness fill our lives with hope for a peaceful journey.

FAITH is...
"Is there faith in death?"
Hope by endurance
Not letting hope die
Conviction of the unseen
Assurance of things
hoped for
What we do not see
Revealed by our hearts
attitude

VIRTUE is...
"Is there hope in death?"
Dealing with the physical
Receiving bad news
Possibly doubting one's
faith
Emotions wrapped
around hope
Presence of goodness
Courage to cope

WHOLENESS is...
"The reality and honesty of death!"
Healing beyond our body
Trust and belief in what is not seen
Path to resolution
Road to peace

How can we give hope to a dying person?

Earlier in chapter six, we learned that being a good listener begins with understanding one's feelings. **Listening** can provide that hope to the dying person. From hospice to attending funerals, we learned to just "be there." A **gift of presence** that is filled with love and support will definitely provide a sense of hope. Children need simple, honest, and direct answers; but so do adults. In death, **knowing the real situation** can allow hope to enter the journey. **Advance Directives** are the official documents that allow us to make our wishes known. When we **support the wishes** of the dying person, then this opens the door for hope of peace and comfort at the end life.

The afterlife

"What happens after death? The mystery of it all." We cannot talk about the mystery of death without talking about the mystery of the afterlife. It is one of the most common questions people share and often a fear that people have when they speak about their own death. Beliefs about the afterlife are often connected to religion and faith traditions. People may be taught from an early age to believe in one particular conviction for what happens when our bodies cease to live. Some have conviction and faith that they die and that is the end of their life as they have known it. Others may have a spiritual component that supports their belief that life continues after death. This belief in an afterlife often brings comfort as people think of their loved ones who have already passed away. It may also provide comfort as they think about their own death. However, even if the belief is in life after death, anxiety may still be present.

Death anxiety

To feel anxiety about death is as common as death itself. Not knowing what will happen or what to expect causes both nervousness and agitation. Usually, those who have strong religious beliefs have less anxiety. Looking at the topics that have been discussed provides some knowledge about the unknown topics of dying and death. Acknowledging that we have decisions to make and that we can be more prepared for this mystifying event will provide some comfort and lessen the anxiety.

As a person ages, courage can be a calming effect that grows through times of anxiety. This courage may provide the realization that death is closer than it used to be and this awareness may bring a stillness that one did not experience at a younger age. Perhaps even the aging process itself helps us in this time as we reflect on our lives. We contemplate what has been important and valuable to us, and we share with those closest to us how we want to be remembered. As we age, we know that death draws closer, which, in turn, may help us to accept the end of our lives more peacefully.

The dignity of it all

There is one principle of a good death that demands attention from both the one who is dying and from the one who cares for the dying.... dignity. Dignity, the quality of being worthy or honored, that does not diminish simply because one is nearing the end of life. It has little to do with outward appearances and more to do with the inner qualities of character, courage, sense of pride, and self-respect. In relation to death, dignity goes right along with hope—it is necessary for all. Dignity starts long before one faces death and is developed throughout a lifetime. It cannot be demanded for ourselves or created for someone else; neither should it be lost in the dying process. The dying person trusts the one who cares for him or her while the caregiver offers respect and honor to the one whose life's final moments are being shared. It is how we face the struggles in our lives; it is a sense of gratitude instead of a sense of entitlement. It is being able to affirm, "What an honor it is to know you." When the end of life arrives, that dignity deepens. We want that person to know we loved him or her dearly and that we will never forget them. We talk, we share. Caring, loving, forgiving...that is what one's life, and one's death, is about. When death does take place, then the dignity turns to honor. It is a time to reflect on memories shared with that loved one. It is time to remember those special times that are embedded in our minds forever and have influenced who we have become today. Dignity compels us to let that person know it was an honor to know him or her and that we hold him or her in the highest esteem. To determine what our own dignity might be, we must ask ourself what we value, what is important to us, what will we be remembered for, and how we will be honored. It is our hope that we will be honored!

The final act...the reality of it!

If you catch a glimpse of a shooting star, the "aaah" and beauty is there and gone in the blink of an eye. The moment is over. People are like that star—we are born, we live, we have those special moments, we say "aaah," and the moment, the life, is over.

Do not wait to say, "I love you." Do not wait to encourage someone. Do not wait to forgive everyone and everything. Do not wait to be that example or role model for someone else. The time is now! Dignity is happening. Each moment must be cherished!

"We die well because we live well...We live well because we know that we will die." We must face our fears. We must make our own decisions. We must be more prepared for this journey. Death is a balancing act. Life is death and death is life.

We have dipped our toes in the water of death. Along the way, we have waded through our attitudes, our fears, and our thoughts about how to have a good death. We have taken a deep breath with each step assuring us that we will be fine when talking about death. We have taken steps to explore our choices that help us make important decisions regarding legal issues. As we have tiptoed through the ripples, we have learned the importance of listening skills and good manners at the end of life. Stepping carefully and gently over the slippery stones, we have considered grief and mourning. As we felt the warm current wrapping around our ankles, we glanced down to see hope and dignity reflected as our companions. The journey of dipping our toes in the water will never end, but it has provided a path of knowledge that is sure to help us with the mystery of dying and death. Now, it is time to enjoy life!

"Live – Love – Forgive like you only have today left."
"Changing the way we die will change the way we live."
"Dying and death is about living life!"

RELECT

Questions to guide your reflection:

What is hope to you?

What is your attitude on death now? Has it changed?

What can you do to live a longer healthier life?

What do you believe in the afterlife... a wall or door? Why?

What causes the most anxiety for you in death?

What is dignity to you?

Let's do a reality check:

>   *What are you going to make of your life?*
>
>   *What are you going to do with your life?*
>
>   *What are you going to get out of life?*
>
>   *What is happening right now?*
>
>   *What are your dreams?*
>
>   *What are you looking forward to?*
>
>   *What makes you happy?*

Quotes to ponder:

"True faith is not only that you believe, but what you believe as well."

"Our parting is not the end of our relationship, it is only an interruption."

"Through the mystery of death, may we see the eternity of life."

"We die well because we live well ... We live well because we know that we will die."

"There is no reason to hope for something that is not possible."

"Hope is fulfilling, but may not always be filled!"

"Hope cannot cure, but can give us encouragement at the end of life!"

REACT

Activity   *Trust Walk*

Instructions:
1. Have each student pick a partner.
2. One partner will be the walker/the other partner will be the leader.
3. Walker: Ties bandana around eyes and rope loosely around ankles.
4. Give each leader a list of directions to a particular spot —not too far from the beginning location. (example: to the office, to a locker, to a particular tree, the tennis courts, etc.)
5. Leader leads the walker to the place and back again. Leader must use good verbal cues and listen to the walker, keeping him or her safe. Walker must listen to the cues carefully and do as the leader says. No peeping!
6. Switch places; leader is walker and walker becomes the leader.
7. Provide new leader with directions to a different location and back.

Reflection: How did you feel?
                     What was most difficult? What was the easiest?
                     What there anything scary?

Activity   *Guest Speaker*

Instructions: Invite someone who has an experience with death of a loved one. (Example: A husband who has lost his wife suddenly and left him with three children.)
1. Have class take notes on speaker's presentation.
2. Reflective thoughts:
   Write down five feelings you felt during the presentation.
3. List four key points or lessons that you learned.

Activity   *Video: Tuesdays with Morrie*

Instructions: Show the video.
Time: 1 ½ hours
1. Complete the worksheet below as you watch the movie.
2. When movie is finished, let class leave in the dark.

Next class: Discussion on the worksheet.
Reflection: 1. What is your perfect day?
                     2. What is the little bird on your shoulder saying to you?

TUESDAYS WITH MORRIE

"Lesson On Living"

Format:

Quotes:	Listen for Morrie's quotes on "lessons learned" and match them to specific topics that are discussed. Write them under the quote section for each topic.
Examples:	While watching the movie, list examples that are portrayed for each specific topic.
Note:	You may need to go back and forth during the movie to complete your list of quotes and examples.
Message:	What do you think the message is? (We will discuss this following the movie.)

Main characters:

Morrie:	Teacher - Dying with Lou Gerrig's disease
Mitch:	Former student of Morrie
Janine:	Mitch's girlfriend

Topic: **Talking about the world?**

Quotes: 1.
         2.
         3.
         4.

Examples of the World:
         1.
         2.
         3.
         4.
         5.

Message:

Topic: **Love?**

Quotes: 1. Love always win
2. Not Giving love but receiving it
3. we think we dont deserve love cause if we let it come in we'll become soft.
4. love is the only rational act

Examples of Love: (this will be throughout the movie)
         1.
         2.
         3.
         4.
         5.

Message:

Topic:

What are we afraid of?
This will be throughout the movie……
List: 5-6 things we are afraid of:
1. Give ~~us~~ ourselfs up to someone we dont want to lose
2. Family
3. Marriage
4. Aging
5. Silence
6. love
7. commitment
8. Dependency

Topic:

The little bird on my shoulder?
Quotes: 1. ~~Is this the day I'm going to die~~
       2. Is this the person I want to be
       3. You won't put the things important off.

Examples: Questions from the little bird?
       1. Is this the day I'm going to die?
       2. Is this the person I want to be?
       3. Am I leading the life I want to lead
       4. Am I ready

Message:
Do the closest thing to your heart

Topic:

Money?
Quotes: 1. Work, money, and   we burrow ourselves in these things
       2.

Examples of Making Money:
       1. Sweat shop
       2.
       3.

Message:

Topic: **Regrets and Forgiving?**

Quotes: 1.

          2.

          3.   ✗

          4.

Examples of Forgiveness (regrets):

1. Morrie regrets showing his dad love
2. Mitch not keeping *not* his promise
3. Morrie forgives himself
4. Janenne forgives mitch

Message:

Pride, vanity, hardening of the heart, He asks yourself why is it so difficult to apologize

Topic: **The Perfect Day?**

Quote: 1.

What was Morrie's "perfect day"? Swimming, lunch/salad, walk in the park, pasta & duck

What was Mitch's "perfect day"? Tuesdays, proposal to Janenne,

Message:

How do you want to live your life.

Topic: **How to say "Good-bye?"**

Quotes: 1. Dont mope around
           2. I will always love you.. you always will
           3. Death end life – not a relationship
           4. If you're in bed – you're dead.

Describe how Morrie taught Mitch to say "good-bye":

1. Spend every tuesdays together
2. Taking care of him
3. Recording him
4. Cries
5. Introduce Janenne

Message:

<u>List four places in the movie that you felt were turning points to the story:</u>

1.

2.

3.

4.

Activity   *Perfect Day*

Instructions: Complete the following sentence:
*If you had 24 hours to live, what would be your
"perfect day"?*

Time you would awake?
Breakfast?

Morning activity?

Lunch?

Afternoon activity?

Dinner?

Evening activity?

Bedtime?

Activity   **My Epitaph**

Instructions: Write and draw your own epitaph (at the top of the next page).

May include a grave marker or statue or both.

Include the following:

Full Name (present)

Date of birth – Date of death (this month)

Any verse or quote of your choice

Activity   *Who Is Most Influential in Your Life NOW?*

Instructions: Ask the question: *Who is most important in your life NOW?*
                    Imagine: That person dies tomorrow.

With that image in mind, answer these questions:
1. What was the happiest moment you recall sharing?

2. What was the saddest moment the two of you shared?

3. What would you miss most?

4. What do you wish you would have said to that person?

5. What do you wish that person would have said to you?

6. What would you have wanted to change in the relationship?

7. What circumstances (time-place-event) do you expect will elicit the most painful memories?

Now, put your head down and close your eyes.
Think about what you wrote!
What feelings are going through your mind?

Activity   *Your Time Runs Out?* *

Instructions: <u>Day Before:</u>   Tell students to bring a magazine that has pictures about health...one that they can cut or tear out...a magazine they do not want.

<u>Day of Activity</u>:
Arrange Room: Push chairs/desks back.
                    Have 8-10 chairs around edge of room facing the outside walls.
Divide the class into groups of 4-6
Time Needed: 50-60 minutes
<u>Materials Needed:</u>
1. 2 timers: 1- for drawing time/1- for the 2 minutes left to work
2. ½ piece of poster board for each group
3. Make available to each group: colored construction paper – white paper - tape (invisible and masking)– glue sticks – markers – crayons – pencils – scissors
4. 4-6 bandanas - blindfolds
5. Basket of participant's names: Slips of paper with each student's name – fold slips and put in a basket
6. Basket of Fates:
    Type the following "messages of fate" on individual slips of paper.

<u>Need 5-6 of each message.</u>

Message 1:
"Your time has run out. All construction materials will be taken from you immediately. Sit quietly in one of the chairs facing the edge of the room for the remainder of the period."

Message 2:
"You have been diagnosed with a terminal illness. You have only 2 remaining minutes to complete your project."

Message 3:
"You have been in a car wreck....You have lost the use of your dominate arm and hand....put that arm behind your back."

Message 4:
"You have suffered a serious set back.... You have become blind with macular degeneration...continue to work without eye sight."
*Fold each individual message and place them in a basket. Throughout the activity, these instructions will be drawn by the chosen student.

*From *Thanatopics: Activities and Exercises for Confronting Death* by J. Eugene Knott, Mary C. Ribar, Betty M. Duson, Marc R. King. Copyright © 1991 by J. Eugene Knott, Mary C. Ribar, Betty M. Duson, Marc R. King. Reprinted by permission of the author.

<u>Fates/Consequences:</u>

Message 1:   Student sits in a chair/desk on outside edge of the room – facing the wall.

Message 2:   Set the timer for 2 minutes – when it goes off, that person moves to the chair/desk on the outside of the room.

Message 3:   Student puts his/her dominate arm behind their back…. they may not use that arm.

Message 4:   Student pretends to be blind – place a blindfold/bandana around student's eyes…must continue to work and not see.

<u>Procedure:</u>

Group Assignment:

1. Each group works together on a health message to present to the class.
2. Use your creativity and any materials the group wants to use.
3. You will have approximately 30 minutes.
4. You will work silently.

Action:

During the time limit, the timer is set to ring at random intervals. Each time the alarm rings, one of the participant's names is drawn from the basket. The instructor goes to that person, taps them on the shoulder. That participant is then required to draw from the "basket of fates" and follow the directions. Keep setting the timer at random times until ¾ of the participants have faced a fate or consequence. The chosen consequence will significantly affect their ability to complete their project as planned.

<u>Debriefing:</u>

Assist the participants in discussing parallels between this exercise and real-life experiences associated with death, loss, and aging.

Questions to ask:

1. What was the experience like for you?
2. What kind of feelings were stirred up inside you each time the alarm rang?
3. How did you feel when you were tapped on the shoulder?
4. How did you feel when you read your instructions?
5. How did you feel when you had to follow your instructions?
6. What kind of reaction did you have toward the instructor?
7. How did you feel toward the other participants?
8. Which fate or consequence do you believe was the most difficult to follow? Why?

9. How might the other participants have assisted you in dealing with your fate if they had been given the opportunity?
10. How do you feel about the quality of your project?
11. Those who were given a setback…what were your reactions? How did the group assist you or did they assist you?
12. How were your feelings similar or dissimilar to the feelings a person might experience in a death, loss, or aging?

Present the projects.
Take up the projects – take them away from the room.
1. What was it like to give up your projects?
2. What feelings did you have when seeing and hearing your project was destroyed?
3. What feelings did you have when the other group's projects were destroyed?
4. What kind of learning did this part of the experience provide you?
5. How did this experience relate to real-life?

RECOMMENDED TERMS/ IMPORTANT PEOPLE/WEBSITES

Terms

Anxiety: Nervousness or agitation about something that is going to happen.

Dignity: "The quality of being worthy, honored, or esteemed."

Hope: "Trust, desire, something hoped for."

Thanatology: Study of death.

Important People

Dr. Ted Powers: Chairman of the Health, Human Performance, and Recreation Department at Baylor University for more than 25 years; Taught till the age of 91; known for his philosophy of life; such an inspiration to all his students!

NOTES

XIV

R.I.P:
Research – Investigate - Present…

"Yes, you have to get up in front of the class"

To teach is to learn…The spotlight is on...
One more thing...Making it mine

GUIDELINES FOR PRESENTATION

Objective: For students to cooperatively participate in researching, writing, and presenting pertinent information on a selected topic relating to "Dying and Death" in order to increase knowledge and confidence as well as ability to talk about death in an open environment.

Possible Points: 75 points   Presentation
<u>25 points</u>   Written: Student Handout
100 points

Grading: The instructor will grade the presentation and the handout.

*Each student of the group will receive an individual grade.

<u>Peer Points:</u>
15 points of the 75 points for the presentation will come from the average score recorded by the students in attendance. Students will receive

a score sheet prior to the presentation. Following the presentation, students will score each individual presenting with a number *1-15* with *1 being low and 15 being high*. The instructor will collect all score sheets and determine the average score for the individual.

*Each group member will also participate in the peer point evaluation.

Grade Sheet:
A grade sheet for the presentation and handout will be returned to each student.

Time Limit: 15 minutes for Lecture
                         15 minutes for Class Activity
                         30 minutes total

Use of Video: No longer than 4 minutes. Video may be used in either the lecture or class activity.

References: Minimum of four required

Presentation: Lecture: 15 minutes
                         The lecture will provide class with important information related to selected topic. (examples: notes, websites, videos, available material)

                         May use posters, technology, demonstrations, bulletin boards, and any other resource that will help to present the material effectively. (* Please know that sometimes the technology may be on the blink—please be prepared with backup! The document camera usually works.)

                         Class Activity: 15 minutes
                         This portion may include a group, partner, or individual activity.

                         You may use creativity in creating an original activity, select an already established activity, or modify one to fit your topic. (examples: game, articles, drawing)

Handout: A handout must be provided for every student in class plus the instructor.

                         You will need _____ handouts.

                         Length: **No more than 3 pages**

                         Due: The day of your presentation

                         Typing Format:
                         1. 1st page: Upper left corner
                             Date
                             Name
                             Course Title
                             Group Members
                             Topic

2. May **_NOT_** be printout of PowerPoint slides
3. Handout outline should include the following:
   A. Introduction of topic.
   B. Outline of *main ideas* and important information pertinent to your topic.
   C. Class Activity: Include the following:
      1). Name and description of activity
      2). Needed supplies/props
      3). Instructions/Rules/Time Limit/Example, etc.
   D. Closure *Big Facts, summary
   E. Bibliography
4. Bibliography: minimum of four resources—books, journal, articles, websites.

Description of Possible Grading Points:

Presentation: Point Values Possible

	Possible Points
Introduction	3 points
Presentation: Major ideas -concepts-unique information	20 points
Organization	5 points
Evidence of Preparation	10 points
Creativity	6 points
Class Participation in Activity	5 points
Closure: Class Questions-Closing Remarks-Summary	6 points
Professionalism: Dress – Speech – Presence	5 points
Peer Points Received (*the average*)	15 points
Any Content Errors? -1@	

TOTAL Points Received   **75 points**

Handout: Point Values Possible

	Possible Points
Clarity	3 points
Organization	5 points
Sufficient/Efficient information (Major Important Points)	10 points
Activity description/Instructions	4 points
Bibliography (at least four resources)	3 points

TOTAL Points   **25 points**

PRESENTATION TOPICS

1. Death as presented in the mass media
2. Death as depicted in music
3. Death as depicted in art
4. Death and religion
5. Cross-cultural perspectives in death
6. War
7. Disaster
8. Homicide
9. Suicide and grief in college students
10. Suicide in the elderly
11. Death of a parent
12. Assisted suicide/Right to die
13. Living with a teriminal illness; living with dying
14. Early pregnancy loss
15. Sudden death
16. Alzheimer's disease
17. Texting and driving
18. Mass killings
19. Gang related deaths
20. Bullying
21. Death by addiction

DYING and DEATH: EVALUATION FORM for PRESENTATION

Date: _____   Groups # _____

Name of Presenter: _____

Topic Presented: _____

	Possible Points	**Points Received**
Introduction:	**3 points**	_____
Presentation (Major Ideas -Concepts-Unique Information)	**20 points**	_____

1.

2.

3.

4.

5.

6.

Organization:	**5 points**	_____
Evidence of Preparation:	**10 points**	_____
Creativity:	**6 points**	_____
Class Participation in Activity:	**5 points**	_____
Closure: (Class Questions-Closing Remarks-Summary)	**6 points**	_____
Professionalism: (Dress – Speech – Presence)	**5 points**	_____
Handout: *(See back for handout grade)*	**25 points**	_____
Peer Points Received *(the average)*	**15 points**	_____
Any Content Errors?	**-1 @**	_____
TOTAL Points Received	**100 points**	_____

Comments:

_____

_____

_____

_____

DYING AND DEATH: EVALUATION FORM
PRESENTATION STUDENT HANDOUT

Presenters in Group: _____

_____

_____

Topic: _____

HANDOUT POINTS (Possible Points: 25)	**Possible Points**	**Points Received**
Clarity:	**3 points**	_____
Organization/Outline Format:	**5 points**	_____
Sufficient and Important Major Idea /Concepts/Information	**10 points**	_____
Activity Description: Activity Name/Supplies/Instructions/Example	**4 points**	_____
Bibliography/Websites: *minimum of 4	**3 points**	_____
TOTAL Points	**Possible Points: 25 points**	_____

Comments:

_____

_____

_____

_____

_____

DYING AND DEATH: PEER POINT EVALUATION FORM

Name of Presenter: _____   **Points Possible: 15**

Topic: _____

Category	Possible Points	My Points	Category	Possible Points	My Points
Introduction	+1	_____	Class Participation in Activity	+1	_____
Major Ideas/Concepts	+3	_____	Closure (class questions/closing summary)	+2	_____
Organization	+2	_____	Professionalism (dress/speech/presence)	+2	_____
Prepared	+2	_____	Handout Information	+1	_____
Creativity	+1	_____	**Any Content Errors**	-1	_____

*Add your points from above.   **My "Total Points" are *(Possible: 15)*?**   _____

Comments: Write 1 reaction and 1 suggestion!

What was: good – helpful - enjoyable? What can be improved?

_____

_____

_____

_____

NOTES

XV
Resources: Films...
"Where is the popcorn?"

Chapter/Film Name: By/Type/Time:

Chapter I: Awareness of Death

Death: The Trip Of A Lifetime: Ambrose film
The Chasm   VHS: 60 minutes

Description: *This film looks at different cultural beliefs and religion in death for Hindu, Death Art, Ghana, Mexico, and Wales.*

Chapter II: Living Every Day

I Heard The Owl Call My Name   Tom Courtenay/Dean Jagger
                                                        VCI Home Film
                                                        VHS: 79 minutes

Description: *A priest, who does not know he is dying, is sent to Canada to minister to an Indian community. There are struggles in understanding the Indians, but these struggles reflect on the priest's own life situation.*

Chapter III: Fears of Death

Death: The Trip Of A Lifetime: Ambrose Film
Going For Glory   VHS: 60 minutes

Description: *This film looks at different cultural beliefs in the afterlife and how these beliefs affect our lives in this world. From Taiwan to Japan to Sydney to Jerusalem to Florida, religious leaders provide their views about the afterlife.*

On Our Own Terms: Moyers On Dying: Public Affairs TV
Living With Dying   VHS: 90 minutes

Description: *This film shares how to overcome fear and denial in death. Patients, families, and caregivers show honesty, courage, and humor in the end of life which can help to make the journey of death a rich experience.*

Round Trip-The Near Death Experience   Wellspring Media
                                             VHS: 40 minutes

Description: *Five people share their stories of their near death experience: terminal illness, scuba diving, childbirth, a bus wreck, and someone's heart stopped. These people provide their personal experience in answering questions like: What happens when we die? Does our spirit live on? Do we meet our deceased friends and relatives? Is it frightening – or wonderful?*

The Forgetting: A Portrait of Alzheimer's Twin City Public Television
                                             DVD: 90 minutes

Description: *This documentary, through panel discussions of experts, weaves together this fearsome disease of actual patients and their caregivers, the history and biology of Alzheimer's, and the struggle to end this disease. These experts provide practical advice with insight of help and hope.*

Chapter IV: A Good Death

Creating A Good Death   ABC News – Nightline
                                             DVD: 26 minutes

Description: *This film follows a patient who is dying with pancreatic cancer. It shares how Laura and her husband cope with a terminal illness in making decisions about her end-of-life issues and striving to have a "good death."*

On Our Own Terms: Moyers On Dying: Public Affairs TV
A Time To Change   VHS: 90 minutes

Description: *The program helps to answer the question…where do you want to die? Caregivers express their goal to improve the care for the dying, including the poor and uninsured.*

Chapter V: Hospice

Life is a Journey

Providence Hospice
VHS: 12:29 minutes

Description: *This film defines hospice, its goals, the role it plays with patients, and how there can be comfort on the end-of life journey.*

On Our Own Terms:
A Different Kind of Care

Moyers on Dying
films for the Humanities & Science
DVD: 87 minutes

Description: *This film presents palliative care, directives, how to balance cost and care, the 5th vital sign, the psychological pain, caring for the poor, the question of nursing homes, leaving the patient in charge, and the end.*

On Our Own Terms:
A Different Kind of Care

Moyers On Dying: Public Affairs TV
VHS: 90 minutes

Description: *This film provides a view into palliative care…pain management and the need for doctors to address the psychological, emotional, physical, and spiritual well-being of patients which will help to relieve the fear of being a burden, of suffering, and of being abandoned during the hour of greatest need.*

Whose Death Is It Anyway?

Independent Production Fund
DVD: 56:26 minutes

Description: *This film presents the tough choices for the end of life. It includes discussion on legal rights, family conflicts, the use of advance directives, palliative care, the choice of dying at home or in a hospital, or dying with hospice care.*

Chapter VI: Listening and Good Manners at the End of Life

Whose Death Is It Anyway?

Independent Production Fund
DVD: 56:26 minutes

Description: *This film presents the tough choices for the end of life. It includes discussion on legal rights, family conflicts, the use of advance directives, palliative care, the choice of dying at home or in a hospital, or dying with hospice care.*

Chapter VII: Physicians and Medical Choices

Before I Die:
Medical Care and Personal Choices

films for the Humanities & Sciences
VHS: 60 minutes

Description: *Panelists are discussing medical and cultural issues, advance directives, palliative care, physician-assisted suicide, the need to re-spiritualize the dying process, and how difficult it is to talk about death.*

Dealing With Death & Dying   Springhouse Corporation
                                                  VHS: 49 minutes

Description: *This film shares insights for health care professionals and how they can
                better deal with the dying patient.*

On Our Own Terms: Moyers On Dying: Public Affairs TV
A Death of One's Own   VHS: 90 minutes

Description: *This film provides a look at the choices at end of life...the reality of
                this debate and the issues surrounding efforts to control the
                circumstances of our death and the implications for families,
                institutions, and communities.*

Chapter VIII: Legal Issues

Difficult Decisions: Films for the Humanities & Sciences
When a Loved One Approaches Death   VHS: 26 minutes

Description: *This film takes a look into life and death decisions inside an ICU – making
                decisions on someone's behalf when they are no longer able to communicate
                their wishes.*

On Our Own Terms: Moyers on Dying
A Different Kind of Care   Films for the Humanities & Science
                                                  DVD: 87 minutes

Description: *This film presents palliative care, directives, how to balance cost and care,
                the 5th vital sign, the psychological pain, caring for the poor, the question of
                nursing homes, leaving the patient in charge, and the end.*

The Doctor Is In...Living Wills   Films for the Humanities & Sciences
                                                  VHS: 30 minutes

Description: *Views are presented from physicians, families, and patients on living
                wills and advance directives. The program includes families and patients
                in intensive care units where they are forced to make decisions on
                lifesaving care.*

Whose Death Is It Anyway?   Independent Production Fund
                                                  DVD: 56:26 minutes

Description: *This film presents the "tough choices for the end of life." It includes a
                discussion on legal rights, family conflicts, advance directives, palliative
                care, the choice of dying at home or in a hospital, or dying with hospice
                care.*

Chapter IX: Today's Debates

On Our Own Terms:	Moyers On Dying: Public Affairs TV
A Death of One's Own	VHS: 90 minutes

Description: *This film provides a look at the choices at end of life...the reality of this debate and the issues surrounding efforts to control the circumstances of our death and the implications for families, institutions, and communities.*

Chapter X: Children and Death

A Child's View of Grief	Connally-Compton Funeral Directors
Picking up the Pieces	VHS: 20 minutes

Description: *This program shares a counselor and actual children who have suffered a loss. From a young age to teenage, these children share how they really feel during grief, what they know, and how they want to be treated. The counselor provides insight on how adults should react and what they can do to help children in grief.*

Hannah's Journey

Hannah's HOPE Ministries
DVD: Short Story: 10 minutes
         Full Story: 32 minutes
         Role of Faith: 20 minutes
         Interview: 11 minutes

Description: *This film shares a short story of Hannah, a teenager and her journey with cancer, how she and her family handled the crisis of a life threatening disease, and the role that faith played in that battle.*

Making Every Moment Count

Fanlight Productions
DVD: 39 minutes

Description: *This film thoughtfully addresses the complex issues involved in end-of-life care for children with life-threatening illnesses. Profiles of five children, their families, and health professionals focus on the emotional and psychological aspects of palliative care in hospitals, a hospice, and at home.*

Chapter XI: Funerals and Body Disposition

Amazing Grace

The Moyers Collections
VHS: 90 minutes

Description: *The song that makes a difference....from St. Paul's Chapel at Columbia University to country western in Nashville, 4-5 performers give their view on what this hymn means to them.*

Death: The Trip of a Lifetime: Ambrose Film
Letting Go   VHS: 60 minutes

Description: *This film provides a view of beliefs and customs in funerals and embalming*
from America to a Ghanaian Village, a drive through funeral parlor in
Florida, and a traditional Buddhist funeral in Japan and how these rituals
affect the way people across the world live their lives.

Chapter XII: Grief – Bereavement – Mourning

A Child's View of Grief   Connally-Compton Funeral Directors
Picking up the Pieces   VHS: 20 minutes

Description: *This program shares a counselor and actual children who have suffered*
a loss. From a young age to teenage, these children share how they really
feel during grief, what they know, and how they want to be treated. The
counselor provides insight on how adults should react and what they can
do to help children in grief.

Depression: Out of the Shadows   PBS Home Film
                                            DVD: 90 minutes

Description: *This film tells dramatic stories of people of different ages and diverse back-*
grounds who live with various forms of depression. Mental health experts
highlight research and innovative treatments which they hope
will provide understanding and hope for the people with this complex, but
treatable disease.

Grief: The Courageous Journey   Films for the Humanities & Sciences
Understanding Grief   VHS: 25 minutes

Description: *This program introduces grief, discusses the forms of grief, and includes*
counseling strategies that helps one begin to understand grief.

Chapter XIII: Hope on the Journey

The Forgetting: A Portrait of Alzheimer's   Twin City Public Television
                                            DVD: 90 minutes

Description: *This documentary, through panel discussions of experts, weaves together*
this fearsome disease of actual patients and their caregivers, the history and
biology of Alzheimer's, and the struggle to end this disease. These experts
provide practical advice with insight of help and hope.

Tuesdays With Morrie   Touchstone Home Entertainment
                                            DVD: 89 minutes

Description: *This movie provides an inspirational story on "the lessons of life" which*
have much to teach us about ourselves.

Bibliography
"Where we found it and who we asked"

CHAPTERS AND REFERENCES

General Resources:

DeSpelder, Lynne Ann, and Strickland, Albert Lee. *The Last Dance*. Boston, MA: McGraw Hill, 2002.

Kastenbaum, Robert J. Death Society and Human Experience. Boston, MA: Pearson Higher Education - Allyn and Bacon, 2009.

Knott, J. Eugene, Ribar, Mary C., Duson, Betty M., and King, Marc R. *Thanatopics: Activities and Exercises for Confronting Death*. Lexington, MA: Lexington Books/D.C. Heath and Company, 1989.

Leming, Michael R. and Dickinson, George, E. *Understanding Dying, Death, & Bereavement*. 6th Edition. Stamford, CT: Thomson Wadsworth Publishing, 2007.

Morrie, Virginia. *Talking About Death Won't Kill You*. New York, NY: Workman Publishing, 2001.

IV.   Good Death

"Creating a Good Death: Coping with Terminal Illness" DVD – ABC News Nightline. Films for the Humanities and Sciences, 2005.

"On Our Own Terms: Moyers on Dying." Four-part film series. Arlington, VA: Educational Broadcasting Company/Public Affairs Television, Inc., 2000.

V.   Hospice

Core Curriculum for the Generalist Hospice and Palliative Nurse. Dubuque, IA: Kendall/Hunt Publishing Company, 2005.

VI.   Listening and Good Manners at the End of Life

Dr. Robert Myrick   University of Florida
                           Developed the "Listening Continuum"

VII.   Physician and Medical Choices

Vox Topics. March 26, 2015. "9 Lessons a Physician Learned About Dying."
   Ezra Klein.

IX.   Today's Debates

Newsweek. September 21, 2009. "I was a teenage death panelist" - Jon Meacham -
   page 8. New York, NY: Newsweek, Inc.

Newsweek. September 21, 2009. "The Case For Killing Granny - Rethinking End of
   Life Care." Thomas Evan. pages 34-40. New York, NY: Newsweek, Inc.

Newsweek. September 21, 2009.   "No Country For Sick Men." T.R. Reid page 42-45.
   New York, NY: Newsweek, Inc.

XII.   Grief – Bereavement – Mourning

Kübler-Ross, Elisabeth. *On Death and Dying.* New York: Macmillan, 1969.

Manning, Doug. The Pain of Grief. Oklahoma City, OK: In-Sight Books, Inc., 2002.

Wolfelt, Alan D. *Healing Your Grieving Heart: 100 Practical Ideas. Ft. Collins, CO:
   Companion Press, 2001*

XIII.   Hope on the Journey

"More Good Years." AARP Magazine (October 2009), pp. 22-24.

"Sidney Poitier – the legendary actor (and author) on life, courage, death, and love."
   AARP Magazine (September/October 2008), pp. 114-115.